Milan Paštéka

SPECTRUM SLOVAKIA Series
Volume 3

On Four Approaches
to density

VEDA
PUBLISHING HOUSE
OF THE SLOVAK ACADEMY OF SCIENCES BRATISLAVA

PETER LANG
INTERNATIONAL ACADEMIC PUBLISHERS

Bibliographic Information published by the Deutsche Nationalbibliothek
The Deutsche Nationalbibliothek lists this publication in the Deutsche Nationalbibliografie; detailed bibliographic data is available in the internet at http://dnb.d-nb.de.

Text © Milan Paštéka

This publication was financially supported UNIVERSITY OF TRNAVA, Faculty of Education, and by the VEGA Grant 2/0206/10.

Issued and printed out by Veda, the publisher of Slovak Academy of Sc Dúbravská cesta 9, 845 02 Bratislava
Number of pages: 97
First edition

ISBN 978-3-631-64941-1
© Peter Lang GmbH
International Academic Publishers
Frankfurt am Main 2013

ISBN 978-80-224-1327-5
© VEDA, SAS Publishing House
Slovak Academy of Sciences
Bratislava 2013

Lang – Frankfurt am Main · Bern · Bruxelles · New York · Oxford

www.peterlang.com   www.veda.sav.sk

Contents

Introduction and basic definitions

The aim of this short book is to present the elements of a systematic theory of certain types of finitely additive probability measures on a set of positive integers. The conventional name of this measures is "density" with an adjective.

Every set of positive integers is finite or infinite countable. It is, thus, impossible to consider a sigma additive probability measure defined on a certain class of the sets of positive integers, which could distinguish between the finite and infinite sets of positive integers. The greatness of the first is negligible. From the point of view of cardinality, the second has the same greatness. If we want to consider the measure of greatness, which could divide the sets of positive integers from a certain aspect of their structure, it is more convenient to consider the finitely additive measure. We shall study four most known types of these set functions.

One of the important rules in the set of positive integers is played by the relation to divisibility, thus our main attention is devoted to the connection between density and this relation. We try to derive some known results from the basic definitions.

I am indebted to Mrs. Rachel N. J. Lees for essential help with the language.

$$* * *$$

We start by the definition of *asymptotic density*. Let us imagine that we choose natural numbers randomly. The intuitive probability with which we pick out an even number is $\frac{1}{2}$, and the same for odd number. Generally for a given m, a positive integer, and r, a non negative integer, the intuitive probability that the selected number is congruent with r modulo m is $\frac{1}{m}$. It is because every interval set $\{1, ..., n\}$ contains approximately $\frac{n}{m}$ elements congruent with r modulo m.

Let the symbol $\mathbb{N}$ denote the set of natural numbers. For $A \subset \mathbb{N}$, and $x \in \mathbb{R}$ ($\mathbb{R}$ will be the set of real numbers), the symbol $A(x)$ denotes the number of elements of A which don't exceed x. Clearly, if χ_A is the indicator function of A, we have

$$A(x) = \sum_{n \leq x} \chi_A(n).$$

The probability that a random number from the set $\{1, ..., n\}$ belongs to the set A is then given by the ratio $\frac{A(n)}{n}$. Now we can define a term which is to be further considered:

The value $\limsup_{x \to \infty} A(x)/x := \overline{d}(A)$ is called the *upper asymptotic density* of A and the value $\liminf_{x \to \infty} A(x)/x := \underline{d}(A)$ is called the lower asymptotic density of A. If $\underline{d}(A) = \overline{d}(A)$, we can say that the set A *has the asymptotic density* and the value

$$d(A) = \lim_{x \to \infty} \frac{A(x)}{x}$$

will be called the *asymptotic density* of the set A.

This set function is a fundamental notion for all following considerations. In the first part we derive its basic properties and some formulas for its calculation for certain types of sets. For instance, Theorem 1, page 14, gives us the possibility to determine the asymptotic density of certain types of set positive integers, defined by the terms of divisibility. In 1951, Ivan Niven in his paper [NIV] proved how zero density of certain types of the sets can be derived from very small parts of these sets. This result is proven on page 20, Theorem 3, using the properties of arithmetic progressions. In the first chapter we also prove certain other formulas for the computation of asymptotic density, later used to prove the classical results of Erdös and Rényi on distribution of the values of additive arithmetic functions. Let us remark that these results are improved recently in [BLS].

R. C. Buck in his work [BUC], 1946, introduced the notion of *measure density*, using the analogy of Jordan measure on real line. This paper defines the system of all finite unions of arithmetic progressions, and the measure density of a given set as the infimum of asymptotic densities of all its oversets from this system. This concept of measure density is studied in the second chapter. A limit formula is proven and the algebra of the measurable set was studied, together with the relation to the uniform distribution of sequences of positive integers.

The notion of uniform distribution of the sequences of the elements of unit interval, defined by H. Weyl in 1916 [WEY], is connected to the density in the same way as the random variable and its distribution function in the theory of probability. Uniform distribution with respect to Buck's measure density is the object of the third chapter. We prove that the well-known Van der Corput sequence is uniformly distributed with respect to Buck's measure density. Then, certain analogy of Weyl's criterion is derived, Theorem 3, page 57. We show that for the case of polyadicly continuous sequences, the uniform distribution and uniform distribution with respect to Buck's measure density coincide. A substantial part of this chapter is copied from the paper [PAS3], with slightly modified proofs of Weyl's criterion based on the characterizations of measurability of sets from previous chapter.

The last two parts are devoted to *uniform density* and *weight density*. The first one is also called *Banach density* by several authors. In this part we quote some results from the number theory seminar of professor Šalát, (1926 - 2005), organized by Comenius University from the sixties practically until the professor's decease.

Several papers are devoted to the permutations preserving the asymptotic density. In the first part, we provide some results about the Levy group originating from [LEV] and studied later in the paper [OB]. Inspired by the latter, we study a certain subgroup of Levy group.

M. B. Nathanson and R. Parikh proved, [NP], that every permutation preserves the asymptotic density if and only if it preserves "having asymptotic density". Later in 2013 J. Bukor, L. Mišík, J. Toth derived more general result. This result is described at the end of the book. The permutations preserving the measure density are studied in the fourth part. This part contains slightly modified results from the paper [PAS5] and the connection between the preserving measure density and uniform distribution of positive integers added, (Theorem 1, page 61).

For each of these concepts, we also study the ideal of sets of zero density and the corresponding generalization of statistical convergence. In the first part we prove the result of [KSW], which characterizes the equivalency between I convergence and I^* convergence, for given I - ideal of sets of positive integers. Let us remark that for the ideal of the sets of 0 asymptotic density we obtain a classical statistical convergence defined in [FH]. Then we apply this characterization to the ideals of zero density for all studied types of densities.

The Asymptotic Density

Let us begin by some simple examples of the sets with an asymptotic density of $\mathbb{N}^2$, the set of all squares. Clearly, $\mathbb{N}^2(x) \leq \sqrt{x}$, thus $d(\mathbb{N}^2) = 0$.

Consider $\alpha > 1$ and β as real numbers. Denote $S = \{[n\alpha + \beta], n \in \mathbb{N}\}$. Then for $x > -\beta$ we have

$$\frac{x - \beta - 1}{\alpha} \leq S(x) \leq \frac{x - \beta}{\alpha},$$

thus $d(S) = \frac{1}{\alpha}$.

We give an example of a set with no asymptotic density: Consider an increasing sequence of positive integers $\{a_n\}$ fulfilling the condition

$$\lim_{n \to \infty} \frac{a_n}{a_1 + \ldots + a_n} = 1.$$

By an easy calculation it can be proven that the set

$$\bigcup_{n=1}^{\infty} (a_{2n}, a_{2n+1}) \cap \mathbb{N}$$

has the upper asymptotic density of 1 and the lower asymptotic density of 0.

We shall denote the set of all subsets of $\mathbb{N}$ having the asymptotic density by the symbol $\mathcal{D}$.

Increasing sequences

The finite sets have the asymptotic density of 0. The following result presents a natural relation between density of an infinite set and the order of its n - th element.

Theorem 1. Let $S \subset \mathbb{N}$ be an infinite set and $S = \{s_1 < s_2 < \ldots\}$. **Then** $S \in \mathcal{D}$ **if and only if there exists a limit** $l = \lim_{n \to \infty} \frac{n}{s_n}$ **and in this case** $l = d(S)$.

Proof. Clearly, $S(s_n) = n$. Thus from $l = d(S)$ it follows $l = \lim_{n \to \infty} \frac{n}{s_n}$. The opposite implication follows from the fact that for $x \in< a_n, a_{n+1})$,

$$\frac{n}{a_{n+1}} \leq \frac{A(x)}{x} \leq \frac{n}{a_n}.$$

$\square$

The following property is well-known as the *Darboux property*:

Corollary 1. Let $A \subset \mathbb{N}$ and $A \in \mathcal{D}$. **Then for every** $\alpha \in< 0, d(A) >$ **there exists** $B \subset A$, $B \in \mathcal{D}$ **that** $d(B) = \alpha$.

Proof. We can suppose that $d(A) > 0$. Put $\beta = \frac{d(A)}{\alpha}$, and if $A = \{a_1 < a_2 < \ldots\}$ then denote $B = \{a_{[\beta n]}; n = 1, 2, \ldots\}$. Clearly $B \subset A$ and from Theorem 1 we obtain $d(B) = \alpha$. $\square$

Corollary 2. If $S = \{s_1 < s_2 < \ldots\}$ **and**

$$\sum_{n=1}^{\infty} \frac{1}{s_n} < \infty$$

then $d(S) = 0$.

Proof. For every $n = 1, 2, \ldots$ we have

$$\frac{n}{s_{2n}} \leq \sum_{k=n}^{2n} \frac{1}{s_k}$$

and

$$\frac{n}{s_{2n+1}} \leq \sum_{k=n}^{2n} \frac{1}{s_k},$$

and the assertion follows from Theorem 1. $\square$

By an easy calculation we obtain:

Corollary 3. A set $A \subset \mathbb{N}$ has asymptotic density if and only if there exists an increasing sequence of positive integers $\{n_k\}$ with $\lim_{k \to \infty} \frac{n_k}{n_{k+1}} = 1$ and the limit $L = \lim_{k \to \infty} \frac{A(n_k)}{n_k}$ exists, and in this case $L = d(A)$.

Basic properties

The following statements we shall use in the following text as the basic properties for study the asymptotic density. The reader can it prove directly from the definition:

i) $\emptyset, \mathbb{N} \in \mathcal{D}$ **and** $d(\emptyset) = 0, d(\mathbb{N}) = 1$,

ii) **every finite subset of $\mathbb{N}$ belongs to $\mathcal{D}$ and its asymptotic density is equal to 0,**

iii) $A \in \mathcal{D}$ **if and only if** $\mathbb{N} \setminus A \in \mathcal{D}$ **and** $d(A) = 1 - d(\mathbb{N} \setminus A)$,

iv) **let** $A, B \in \mathcal{D}$ **then** $A \cup B \in \mathcal{D}$ **if and only if** $A \cap B \in \mathcal{D}$ **and in this case** [i]

$$d(A) + d(B) = d(A \cap B) + d(A \cup B).$$

v) **if** $A, B \subset \mathbb{N}$ **and** $A \subset B$ **then** $\underline{d}(A) \leq \underline{d}(B)$ **and** $\overline{d}(A) \leq \overline{d}(B)$**, if moreover** $A, B \in \mathcal{D}$ **then** $B \setminus A \in \mathcal{D}$ **and** $d(B \setminus A) = d(B) - d(A)$,

vi) **if** $A \in \mathcal{D}$ **and** $d(A) = 1$ **then for every** $B \subset \mathbb{N}$ **it holds** $B \in \mathcal{D}$ **if and only if** $A \cap B \in \mathcal{D}$ **and in this case** $d(B) = d(A \cap B)$.
Let $A \subset \mathbb{N}, m \in \mathbb{N}, r \in \mathbb{Z}$, let us denote

$$mA = \{ma; a \in A\}, A + r = \{a + r, a \in A\} \cap \mathbb{N},$$

then

vii) $A + r \in \mathcal{D}, mA \in \mathcal{D}$ **if and only if** $A \in \mathcal{D}$ **and in this case** $d(A + r) = d(A)$ **and** $d(mA) = \frac{1}{m} d(A)$.
Put $r + (m) = \{x \in \mathbb{N}; x \equiv r \pmod{m}\}$, instead of $0 + (m)$ we shall write only (m). These sets are called the *arithmetic progressions*.
Clearly there is a finite number of elements of $(m) + r$ which do not belong to $r + (m)$.

---

[i] The examples of sets which belong to $\mathcal{D}$ with intersection not belonging to $\mathcal{D}$ we construct in the proof of Theorem A on the page 35.

viii) **For every** $m \in \mathbb{N}, r \in \mathbb{Z}$ **we have** $r + (m) \in \mathcal{D}$ **and**
$$d(r + (m)) = \tfrac{1}{m}.$$

Let us remark that a system of sets $\mathcal{A}$ such that $\mathbb{N} \in \mathcal{A}$, $A \in \mathcal{A} \Rightarrow \mathbb{N} \setminus A \in \mathcal{A}$ and for $A, B \in \mathcal{A}$ it holds $A \cup B \in \mathcal{A}$ if and only if $A \cap B \in \mathcal{A}$ is called q-*algebra*. Thus the system $\mathcal{D}$ is q-algebra.

We continue by the results of paper [SaS] where the sets related to the canonical representation have been studied and their asymptotic density was computed directly from the definition.

Let $n \in \mathbb{N}$ with the canonical representation $n = p_1^{\alpha_1}...p_s^{\alpha_s}$. Let us denote $H(n) = \max\{\alpha_1, ..., \alpha_s\}$. Define moreover, for a prime number p, the value $\alpha_p(n)$ the exponent of p from the canonical representation of n.

The symbol $\zeta(k), k > 1$ shall be used for the well known Riemanian zeta function defined as follows

$$\zeta(k) = \sum_{n=1}^{\infty} \frac{1}{n^k} = \prod_{p} \left(1 - \frac{1}{p^k}\right)^{-1}.$$

Proposition A: Let $k \in \mathbb{N}$. **Put** $R_k = \{n \in \mathbb{N}; k | n \wedge H(n) \le k\}$. **Then** $R^k \in \mathcal{D}$ **and**

$$d(R^k) = \zeta(k+1)^{-1} \prod_{p|k} \frac{p^{k-\alpha_p(k)+1} - 1}{p^{k+1} - 1}.$$

Proof: The proof is based on the estimation of the value $R_k(n), n \in \mathbb{N}$. Through this proof we shall use the symbol $\delta(n), n \in \mathbb{N}$ for the moebius function of n because μ will bear another meaning [ii].

Clearly

$$\sum_{m^{k+1}|n} \delta(m) = 1 \Longleftrightarrow H(n) \le k,$$

$$\sum_{m^{k+1}|n} \delta(m) = 0 \text{ otherwise.}$$

Thus we have

$$R_k(n) = \sum_{j \le \frac{n}{k}} \sum_{m^{k+1}|jk} \delta(m) = \sum_{m \le n^{\frac{1}{k+1}}} \delta(m) \sum_{j \le \frac{n}{k}, m^{k+1}|jk} 1 =$$

$$= \sum_{m \le n^{\frac{1}{k+1}}} \delta(m) \left[\frac{(m^{k+1}, k)n}{m^{k+1}k}\right] = \frac{n}{k} \sum_{m \le n^{\frac{1}{k+1}}} \delta(m) \frac{(m^{k+1}, k)}{m^{k+1}} + O\left(n^{\frac{1}{k+1}}\right).$$

Thus

$$\lim_{n \to \infty} \frac{R_k(n)}{n} = \frac{1}{k} \sum_{m=1}^{\infty} \delta(m) \frac{(m^{k+1}, k)}{m^{k+1}}.$$

[ii] $\delta(1) = 1$, $\delta(n) = 0$ if $p^2 | n$ for a prime p and $\delta(n) = (-1)^k$ if $n = p_1...p_k$, where p_j are different primes. For the basic properties of this function we refer to books on elementary number theory.

The infinite series on the right hand side converges absolutely and the function $\delta(m)\frac{(m^{k+1},k)}{m^{k+1}}$ is multiplicative. Thus

$$d(R_k) = \frac{1}{k}\prod_p\left(1 - \frac{(p^{k+1},k)}{p^{k+1}}\right) =$$

$$= \prod_p\left(1 - \frac{1}{p^{k+1}}\right)\prod_{p|k}\left(\frac{1}{(p^{k+1},k)} - \frac{1}{p^{k+1}}\right)\frac{p^{k+1}}{p^{k+1}-1} =$$

$$= \zeta(k+1)^{-1}\prod_{p|k}\frac{p^{k-\alpha_p(k)+1}-1}{p^{k+1}-1}.$$

$\square$

Analogously, it can be proven:

Proposition B: Let $k \in \mathbb{N}$. Put $L_k = \{n \in \mathbb{N}; k|n \wedge H(n) < k\}$. Then $L_k \in \mathcal{D}$ and

$$d(L_k) = \zeta(k)^{-1}\prod_{p|k}\frac{p^{k-\alpha_p(k)}-1}{p^k-1}.$$

Union of the arithmetic progressions

From certain point of view, the arithmetic progressions have an analogical rule in the set of positive integers as the intervals on the real line. The following result gives us the possibility to calculate the asymptotic density of certain sets which can be described using the union of arithmetic progressions.

We shall use the following simple property:

ix) **Arbitrary set $S \subset \mathbb{N}$ belongs to $\mathcal{D}$ if and only if for every $\varepsilon > 0$ there exists the set $S_1 \in \mathcal{D}$ such that $S_1 \subset S$ and $\overline{d}(S\backslash S_1) < \varepsilon$. And in this case $d(S_1) \leq d(S) \leq d(S_1)+\varepsilon$.**

This is equivalent with:

Arbitrary set $S \subset \mathbb{N}$ belongs to $\mathcal{D}$ if and only if there exist the sets $S_k \in \mathcal{D}, k \in \mathbb{N}$ such that $S_k \subset S, k \in \mathbb{N}$ and $\lim_{k\to\infty}\overline{d}(S \setminus S_k) = 0$. And in this case $d(S) = \lim_{k\to\infty}d(S_k)$.

Theorem 1. Let $\{m_k\}$ be a sequence of positive integers such that $(m_i, m_j) = 1$ for $i \neq j$. **Then**

a) **for $N = 1, 2, \ldots$ and arbitrary sequence of integers $r_1, r_2, \ldots$ it holds $\bigcup\limits_{k=1}^{N} r_k + (m_k) \in \mathcal{D}$**

and

$$d\left(\bigcup_{k=1}^{N} r_k + (m_k)\right) = 1 - \prod_{k=1}^{N}\left(1 - \frac{1}{m_k}\right).$$

b) $\bigcup\limits_{k=1}^{\infty}(m_k) \in \mathcal{D}$ **and**

$$d\left(\bigcup_{k=1}^{\infty}(m_k)\right) = 1 - \prod_{k=1}^{\infty}\left(1 - \frac{1}{m_k}\right).$$

Proof. Due to the Chinese reminder theorem, we have

$$\bigcap_{j=1}^{s} r_{k_j} + (m_{k_j}) = r + (m_{k_1}...m_{k_s})$$

for a suitable r. Thus the part a) can be derived by induction or by the exclusion inclusion principle.

For the proof of the part b) we shall consider two cases

i) $\sum_{k=1}^{\infty} \frac{1}{m_k} = \infty$

ii) $\sum_{k=1}^{\infty} \frac{1}{m_k} < \infty$

Case i) Put $A_n = \bigcup_{k=1}^{n} (m_k)$. Then $A_n \subset A$, where $A = \bigcup_{k=1}^{\infty} (m_k)$. Thus for $n = 1, 2, \ldots$ and $x \in R$ we have $A_n(x) \leq A(x)$, this yields

$$\frac{A_n(x)}{x} \leq \frac{A(x)}{x}.$$

And so for $x \to \infty$ we obtain

$$1 - \prod_{k=1}^{n} \left(1 - \frac{1}{m_k}\right) \leq \underline{d}(A).$$

Using the inequality $1 - x \leq e^{-x}, x \geq 0$, we get $\prod_{k=1}^{n} \left(1 - \frac{1}{m_k}\right) < e^{-\sum_{k=1}^{n} \frac{1}{m_k}}$ and so in this case

it holds $\prod_{k=1}^{\infty} \left(1 - \frac{1}{m_k}\right) = 0$. Thus for $n \to \infty$ we have $d(A) = 1$.

Case ii) Let $A, A_n, n = 1, 2, \ldots$ have the same meaning as in the case i). Let us put moreover $S_n = \bigcup_{k=n+1}^{\infty} (m_k)$. Then $A \setminus A_n \subset S_n$. $S_n(x)$ satisfies the inequality $S_n(x) \leq \sum_{k=n+1}^{\infty} \left[\frac{x}{m_k}\right] < x \sum_{k=n+1}^{\infty} \frac{1}{m_k}$, and so $\overline{d}(S_n) \leq \sum_{k=n+1}^{\infty} \frac{1}{m_k}$. Hence the condition ii) implies $\lim_{n \to \infty} \overline{d}(S_n) = 0$ and the assertion follows from ix). □

An equivalent form of the theorem is proven in [NAR]. A stronger form is in [HR].

Remark. In the previous theorem, part b) can be not extended to the case of the union of arbitrary arithmetic progressions as in the part a) as the following example shows:

$$\bigcup_{k=1}^{\infty} k + (m_k) = \mathbb{N}.$$

Corollary 1. If, in the previous theorem, it holds $\sum_{k=1}^{\infty} \frac{1}{m_k} = \infty$ then $d\left(\bigcup_{k=1}^{\infty} (m_k)\right) = 1$.

Corollary 2. Let $P = \{p_1, p_2, ...\}$ be such a set of primes that $\sum_{k=1}^{\infty} \frac{1}{p_k} = \infty$. Denote by H the set of all positive integers which are not divisible by the elements of P. Then $H \in \mathcal{D}$ and $d(H) = 0$.

A subset of $\mathbb{N}$ is called *closed to divisibility* or in short *CD - set* if and only if it contains all positive divisors of every element and with every two elements it contains its last common multiple. If A is a CD - set and $p_j, j = 1, 2, \ldots$ is finite or infinite sequence of all such primes of which certain power does not belong to A, then this set can be represented in the following form

$$A = \mathbb{N} \setminus \bigcup_j (p_j^{\alpha_j}),$$

where α_j is the minimal exponent α that $p_j^\alpha \notin A$. Thus $A \in \mathcal{D}$ and

$$d(A) = \prod_j \left(1 - \frac{1}{p_j^{\alpha_j}}\right).$$

A well-known CD-set is the set Q_2 of all positive integers which contain only the first powers of primes in the canonical decomposition. This set contains p but does not contain p^2 for every prime number p. From the last formula we get

$$d(Q_2) = \prod_p \left(1 - \frac{1}{p^2}\right) = \frac{6}{\pi^2}.$$

Similarly as Theorem 1 can be proven:

Proposition: Let $\{m_j\}, \{n_s\}$ be two sequences of relatively prime positive integers such that $(m_j, n_s) = 1, j, s \in \mathbb{N}$. Then

a) **For every $M, N \in \mathbb{N}$ the set $S_{M,N} = (\cup_{j=1}^M (m_j)) \cap (\cup_{s=1}^N (n_s))$ belongs to $\mathcal{D}$ and**

$$d(S_{M,N}) = \left(1 - \prod_{j=1}^M \left(1 - \frac{1}{m_j}\right)\right)\left(1 - \prod_{s=1}^N \left(1 - \frac{1}{n_s}\right)\right).$$

b) **For every $N \in \mathbb{N}$ the set $S_N = (\cup_{j=1}^\infty (m_j)) \cap (\cup_{s=1}^N (n_s))$ belongs to $\mathcal{D}$ and**

$$d(S_N) = \left(1 - \prod_{j=1}^\infty \left(1 - \frac{1}{m_j}\right)\right)\left(1 - \prod_{s=1}^N \left(1 - \frac{1}{n_s}\right)\right).$$

c) **The set $S = (\cup_{j=1}^\infty (m_j)) \cap (\cup_{s=1}^\infty (n_s))$ belongs to $\mathcal{D}$ and**

$$d(S) = \left(1 - \prod_{j=1}^\infty \left(1 - \frac{1}{m_j}\right)\right)\left(1 - \prod_{s=1}^\infty \left(1 - \frac{1}{n_s}\right)\right).$$

The property ix) implies:

**Proposition C: Let $A_k, k \in \mathbb{N}$ be mutually disjoint sets from $\mathcal{D}$ such that $\lim\limits_{N \to \infty} \overline{d}(\cup_{k=N}^{\infty} A_k)=$
0. Then $B = \cup_{k=1}^{\infty} A_k$ belongs to $\mathcal{D}$ and**

$$d(B) = \sum_{k=1}^{\infty} d(A_k).$$

Now we can prove one of the main results from [SaS]:

Theorem: Let $M_H = \{n \in \mathbb{N}; H(n)|n\}$ then $M_H \in \mathcal{D}$ and

$$d(M_H) = \zeta(2) + \sum_{k=2}^{\infty} \zeta(k+1)^{-1} \prod_{p|k} \frac{p^{k-\alpha_p(k)+1}-1}{p^{k+1}-1} - \zeta(k)^{-1} \prod_{p|k} \frac{p^{k-\alpha_p(k)}-1}{p^k-1}.$$

Proof: By the notation from Proposition A and Proposition B, we have $L_k \subset R_k, k = 1, 2, ...$ and $R_k \subset L_k = \{n \in \mathbb{N}; H(n) = k \wedge k|n\}$. Thus

$$M_H = R_1 \cup \bigcup_{k=2}^{\infty} (R_k \setminus L_k).$$

R_1 is the the set of square free integers and the sets $R_k \setminus L_k, k \in N$ are mutually disjoint. Moreover, $\cup_{k=N}^{\infty}(R_k \setminus L_k) \subset \{n \in \mathbb{N}; H(n) \geq N\}$ thus $\overline{d}(\cup_{k=N}^{\infty}(R_k \setminus L_k)) \leq 1 - \zeta(N+1)$. We have $\lim_{N \to \infty} 1 - \zeta(N+1) = 0$ and the assertion follows from Propositions A,B,C. $\square$

Using the ideas from the proof of Theorem 1, we can prove the following statement, which can be useful for the calculation of asymptotic density of certain sets:

Proposition I: Let $A_k \in \mathcal{D}$ and $\{m_k\}$ be such a sequence of positive integers that $\sum_k \frac{1}{m_k} < \infty$ and the sets $m_k A_k, k = 1, 2, ..$ are mutually disjoint. Then the set $\cup_k m_k A_k$ belongs to $\mathcal{D}$ and

$$d\left(\bigcup_k m_k A_k\right) = \sum_k \frac{d(A_k)}{m_k}.$$

Proof: Suppose that the sequence $\{m_k\} = \{m_1, ..., m_s\}$ is finite. Put $B = \cup_{k=1}^{s} m_k A_k$. Then condition of disjointness yields

$$B(n) = \sum_{k=1}^{s} A_k\left(\frac{n}{m_k}\right)$$

for every $n \in \mathbb{N}$. Thus

$$B(n) = \sum_{k=1}^{s} A_k\left(\frac{n}{m_k}\right)$$

$$\lim_{n \to \infty} \frac{B(n)}{n} = \sum_{k=1}^{s} \frac{d(A_k)}{m_k}.$$

The assertion is proven for the finite case of $\{m_k\}$. Let this sequence be infinite. Let us denote $C = \cup_{k=1}^{\infty} m_k A$ and $B_s = \cup_{k=1}^{s} m_k A_k$ for $s \in \mathbb{N}$. Then $C \setminus B_s \subset \cup_{k=s+1}^{\infty} m_k A_k$ and so for every $n \in \mathbb{N}$ we have

$$(C \setminus B_s)(n) \le \sum_{k=s+1}^{\infty} (m_k A_k)(n) \le n \sum_{k=s+1}^{\infty} \frac{1}{m_k}$$

thus

$$\overline{d}(C \setminus B_s) \le \sum_{k=s+1}^{\infty} \frac{1}{m_k}.$$

From the convergence of the infinite series $\sum_{k=1}^{\infty} \frac{1}{m_k}$ we deduce $\lim_{s \to \infty} \overline{d}(C \setminus B_s) = 0$ and the statement follows from ix). $\qquad\square$

Let $n = p_1^{\alpha_1} ... p_r^{\alpha_r}$ be the canonical representation of the positive integer n. Put $\omega(n) = r$ and $\Omega(n) = \alpha_1 + ... + \alpha_r$. In the paper [Re1] the sets

$$E_k = \{n;\ \Omega(n) - \omega(n) = k\},\ k = 0, 1, ...$$

are studied. Clearly, the set E_0 is the sets of square free integers.

Now we shall follow the ideas from [Re1] using Proposition I.

Every integer n can be uniquely represented in the form $n = PS$, where P, S are relatively primes and S is a square free integer and P is 1 or in the form $P = q_1^{\beta_1} ... q_s^{\beta_s}$ where $2 \le \beta_1 \le ... \le \beta_s$. The finite non decreasing sequence $\beta = \{\beta_1, ..., \beta_s\}$ is called the *signature* of n.

Let $S(\beta)$ denote the set of all positive integers with the signature β. If $q_1, ..., q_s$ then $F(q_1, ..., q_s)$ will denote the set

$$F(q_1, ..., q_s) = \mathbb{N} \setminus \left((q_1) \cup ... \cup (q_s) \cup \bigcup_{p \ne q_j, j=1,...,s} (p^2) \right).$$

Theorem 1 implies that $F(q_1, ..., q_s) \in \mathcal{D}$, and

$$d(F(q_1, ..., q_s)) = \left(1 - \frac{1}{q_1}\right) ... \left(1 - \frac{1}{q_s}\right) \prod_{p \ne q_j, j=1,...,s} \left(1 - \frac{1}{p^2}\right).$$

If $\beta = \{\beta_1, ..., \beta_s\}$ then the set $S(\beta)$ can be expressed as disjoint union

$$S(\beta) = \bigcup_{[q_1,...,q_s]} q_1^{\beta_1} ... q_s^{\beta_s} F(q_1, ..., q_s)$$

where the last union goes through all s tuples of different primes $q_1, ..., q_s$. Since $\beta_j \ge 2, j = 1, ..., s$ the infinite series

$$\sum_{[q_1,...,q_s]} \frac{1}{q_1^{\beta_1} ... q_s^{\beta_s}}$$

converges and so Proposition I implies that $S(\beta) \in \mathcal{D}$ and

$$d(S(\beta)) = \frac{6}{\pi^2} \sum_{[q_1,\ldots,q_s]} \frac{1}{(q_1 + 1)q_1^{\beta_1 - 1} \ldots (q_s + 1)q_s^{\beta_s - 1}},$$

where the summation runs over all s tuples of different prime numbers $[q_1, \ldots, q_s]$. For $n \in S(\beta)$ there holds $\Omega(n) - \omega(n) = (\beta_1 - 1) + \ldots + (\beta_s - 1)$. Therefore the set E_k is a disjoint union of the sets $S(\beta)$ where $\beta_1 - 1 + \ldots + \beta_s - 1 = k$. Only a finite number of such signatures β exists. And so we have:

Proposition II: For every $k = 0, 1, \ldots$ we have $E_k \in \mathcal{D}$ and

$$d(E_k) = \sum_{\beta_1 + \ldots + \beta_s - s = k} d(S(\beta)).$$

After certain calculations, we get the generating function for the densities $d(E_k), k = 0, 1 \ldots$

$$\sum_{k=0}^{\infty} d(E_k)z^k = \frac{6}{\pi^2} \prod_{p-prime} \left(1 + \frac{1}{p+1}\left(\frac{z}{p} + \frac{z^2}{p^2} + \ldots\right)\right)$$

for every complex number z that $|z| < 2$. If we put $z = 1$ we get

$$\sum_{k=0}^{\infty} d(E_k) = 1. \tag{I}$$

Direct factors

Let $A, B \subset \mathbb{N}$. We say that $\mathbb{N}$ is the *direct product* of A, B, shortly $\mathbb{N} = A \odot B$, if and only if every positive integer n can be uniquely represented in the form $n = ab$, $a \in A, b \in B$. In this case, the sets A, B are called the *direct factors*. In 1978, P. Erdös, B. Saffari, R.C. Vaughan proved the following result, regarding the asymptotic density of direct factors, (see [ESV], [SAF]).

Theorem 2. Let $\mathbb{N} = A \odot B$ then $A, B \in \mathcal{D}$ and

$$d(A) = \left(\sum_{b \in B} \frac{1}{b}\right)^{-1}.$$

We present the proof of the result of H. Daboussi from [DAB]. He uses the Dirichlet convolution of arithmetic functions, and the following equality: **Let f, g be two nonnegative arithmetic functions, such that the infinite series $\sum_{n=1}^{\infty} \frac{f(n)}{n}, \sum_{n=1}^{\infty} \frac{g(n)}{n}, \sum_{n=1}^{\infty} \frac{(f*g)(n)}{n}$ converge. Then**

$$\sum_{n=1}^{\infty} \frac{f(n)}{n} \cdot \sum_{n=1}^{\infty} \frac{g(n)}{n} = \sum_{n=1}^{\infty} \frac{(f*g)(n)}{n}. \tag{i}$$

This equality can be derived by direct calculation.

Let y be a positive real number. Define two arithmetic functions, u_y, v_y as follows: $u_y(n) = 1$ if and only if all prime divisors of n exceed y, otherwise $u_y(n) = 0$. Consider the set $M_y = \mathbb{N} \setminus \cup_{p \leq y}(p)$. For $x > 0$ there holds $\sum_{n \leq x} u_y(n) = M_y(x)$ and so Theorem 1 implies

$$\lim_{x \to \infty} \frac{1}{x} \sum_{n \leq x} u_y(n) = \prod_{p \leq y} \left(1 - \frac{1}{p}\right). \qquad (ii)$$

We shall define the function v_y in a certain sense in the opposite way: $v_y(n) = 1$ if the canonic decomposition of n contains only the primes not exceeding y, and $v_y(n) = 0$ otherwise. If $p_1, ..., p_s$ are all primes till y, then using the formula for the sum of geometric progression we get

$$\sum_{n=1}^{\infty} \frac{v_y(n)}{n} = \sum \frac{1}{p_1^{\alpha_1} ... p_s^{\alpha_s}} = \prod_{p \leq y} \left(1 - \frac{1}{p}\right)^{-1}. \qquad (iii)$$

Clearly, $v_y(n_1 n_2) = v_y(n_1) v_y(n_2)$ for $n_1, n_2 \in \mathbb{N}$. This yields that for the arbitrary arithmetic functions f, g, it holds

$$(v_y f) * (v_y g) = v_y(f * g). \qquad (iv)$$

Let α be the indicator function of A and β the indicator function of B. From $\mathbb{N} = A \odot B$ we obtain

$$\alpha * \beta = 1. \qquad (v)$$

Put for $x > 0$

$$A_y(x) = \sum_{n \leq x} ((v_y \alpha) * u_y)(n).$$

We can prove by simple calculations that

$$A_y(x) = \sum_{d \leq x} v_y(d) \alpha(d) \sum_{k \leq \frac{x}{d}} u_y(k). \qquad (vi)$$

The following two lemmas will be crucial in the proof of Theorem 2.
Lemma 1.

$$\lim_{x \to \infty} \frac{1}{x} A_y(x) = \left(\sum_{b \in B} \frac{v_y(b)}{b}\right)^{-1}.$$

Proof. Equality (vi) implies

$$\frac{1}{x} A_y(x) = \sum_{d \leq x} \frac{v_y(d) \alpha(d)}{d} \frac{d}{x} \sum_{k \leq \frac{x}{d}} u_y(k), x > 0$$

and so by (ii) and (iii) we get

$$\lim_{x \to \infty} \frac{1}{x} A_y(x) = \sum_{d=1}^{\infty} \frac{v_y(d) \alpha(d)}{d} \left(\sum_{d=1}^{\infty} \frac{v_y(d)}{d}\right)^{-1}. \qquad (vii)$$

The equalities (iv) and (v) imply $v_y = (v_y\alpha) * (v_y\beta)$ and thus by (iv) we have

$$\sum_{b=1}^{\infty} \frac{v_y(b)}{b} = \left(\sum_{b=1}^{\infty} \frac{v_y(b)\alpha(b)}{b} \right) \left(\sum_{b=1}^{\infty} \frac{v_y(b)\beta(b)}{b} \right),$$

and the assertion follows from (vii).   □

Lemma 2. For $x > 0, y > 0$ it holds

$$A(x) \leq A_y(x).$$

Proof. It can be easily verified that $v_y * u_y = 1$ and so analogously as in previous evidence, we get $(v_y\alpha) * (v_y\beta) * u_y = 1$. In the other form

$$\sum_{abc=n} v_y(a)\alpha(a)v_y(b)\beta(b)u_y(c) = 1, \ n = 1, 2, ...,$$

and this is the same as

$$\sum_{abc=n, a\in A, b\in B} v_y(a)v_y(b)u_y(c) = 1, \ n = 1, 2, ...$$

Therefore it holds

$$A(x) = \sum_{n\leq x} \alpha(n) \sum_{abc=n, a\in A, b\in B} v_y(a)v_y(b)u_y(c).$$

By the transformation of the right side we obtain

$$A(x) = \sum_{a\leq x, a\in A} v_y(a) \sum_{c\leq \frac{x}{a}} u_y(c) \sum_{b\leq \frac{x}{ac}, b\in B} v_y(b)\alpha(abc).$$

We show that in the last sum, at most, one summand is nonzero. Suppose $b_1ac := a_1 \in A, b_2ac := a_2 \in A$. Then $b_1a_2 = b_2a_1$ and from $\mathbb{N} = A \odot B$ we get $b_1 = b_2$. We see that the last sum does not exceed 1, this yields

$$A(x) \leq \sum_{a\leq x, a\in A} v_y(a) \sum_{c\leq \frac{x}{a}} u_y(c).$$

Thus the assertion follows from (vi).   □

Now we can start the proof of Theorem 2. From the definition of the function v_y it follows that for each $b \in \mathbb{N}$ it holds $v_y(b) = 1$ if y exceeds all prime divisors of b. Therefore,

$$\lim_{y\to\infty} \sum_{b\in B} \frac{v_y(b)}{b} = \sum_{b\in B} \frac{1}{b}, \tag{viii}$$

also in case the series on the right hand side diverges. Thus, in this case of Theorem 2, it follows immediately from Lemma 1 and Lemma 2. Thus we can suppose that

$$\sum_{b\in B} \frac{1}{b} < \infty. \tag{ix}$$

The set $\mathbb{N}$ is the direct product of A, B. Therefore $\mathbb{N} = \cup_{b \in B} bA$ is a disjoint decomposition. Thus for $x > 0$ we have

$$[x] = \sum_{b \in B, b \leq x} A\left(\frac{x}{b}\right).$$

Dividing the last inequality by x and bounding the summands by Lemma 2 we see that

$$\frac{[x]}{x} - \sum_{b \in B, 1 < b \leq x} \frac{1}{b} \frac{b}{x} A_y\left(\frac{x}{b}\right) \leq \frac{A(x)}{x} \leq \frac{A_y(x)}{x}.$$

Right hand side converges by Lemma 1, for $x \to \infty$ to $\left(\sum_{b \in B} \frac{v_y(b)}{b}\right)^{-1}$, and the left hand side to

$$1 - \left(\sum_{b \in B} \frac{v_y(b)}{b}\right) \sum_{1 < b \in B} \frac{1}{b} = 1 - \left(\sum_{b \in B} \frac{v_y(b)}{b}\right)^{-1} \sum_{b \in B} \frac{1}{b} + \left(\sum_{b \in B} \frac{v_y(b)}{b}\right)^{-1}.$$

Thus both sides converge by (viii) and (ix) for $y \to \infty$ to $\left(\sum_{b \in B} \frac{1}{b}\right)^{-1}$, and Theorem 2 is proven. $\qquad\square$

Density zero

In 1951 Ivan Niven proved the result which can help determine that the set has density zero by analyzing very small parts of this set. Let $S \subset \mathbb{N}$ and p - prime. Denote by S_p the subset of S which contains all elements from S divisible by p but not divisible by p^2.

Theorem 3. Let $\{p_n\}$ be such a sequence of different primes that

$$\sum_{n=1}^{\infty} \frac{1}{p_n} = \infty. \qquad (*)$$

Then for arbitrary set $S \subset \mathbb{N}$ it holds

$$d(S) = 0 \iff \forall n = 1, 2, ...; d(S_{p_n}) = 0.$$

In the original paper [NIV] the proof is based on the estimation of the value $S(x), x > 0$. Our proof uses the properties of arithmetic progressions.

Proof. In fact $S_p = S \cap ((p) \setminus (p^2))$. Let us denote

$$M_N = \mathbb{N} \setminus \bigcup_{n=1}^{N} ((p_n) \setminus (p_n^2)).$$

Clearly,

$$S \subset S_{p_1} \cup ... \cup S_{p_N} \cup M_N. \qquad (**)$$

We prove by induction that

$$d(M_N) = \prod_{n=1}^{N} \left(1 - \frac{1}{p_n} + \frac{1}{p_n^2}\right). \qquad (***)$$

The equality $(* * *)$ holds trivially for $N = 1$. Assume $(* * *)$ for N. We have

$$M_{N+1} = M_N \setminus ((p_{N+1}) \setminus (p_{N+1}^2)) =$$

$$= M_N \setminus (M_N \cap (p_{N+1}) \setminus M_N \cap (p_{N+1}^2)).$$

The set M_N can be represented as a disjoint union of arithmetic progressions of the form $r_i + (p_1^2 ... p_N^2)$. Due to the Chinese reminder theorem the intersection $M_N \cap (p_{N+1})$ can be represented as the same number of the arithmetic progressions of the form $z_i + (p_1^2 ... p_N^2 p_{N+1})$, thus $d(M_N \cap (p_{N+1})) = \frac{1}{p_{N+1}} d(M_N)$, analogously we can see that $d(M_N \cap (p_{N+1}^2)) = \frac{1}{p_{N+1}^2} d(M_N)$. And so by an easy calculation we obtain that $(* * *)$ holds for $N + 1$.

And so, if $\forall n = 1, 2, ...; d(S_{p_n}) = 0$ we see from $(* *)$ and $(* * *)$ that

$$\overline{d}(S) \leq \prod_{n=1}^{N} \left(1 - \frac{1}{p_n} + \frac{1}{p_n^2}\right),$$

and the assumption $(*)$ yields that the right hand side tends to 0 as $N \to \infty$. The opposite implication is trivial. $\square$

Consider now for instance the set S of all positive integers having only the exponents exceeding 1 in the canonical representation. Then $S_p = \emptyset$ for every prime number p, therefore Theorem 3 implies $d(S) = 0$.

Let us denote for $k = 1, 2, ...$ by $\mathbb{N}(k)$ the set of all positive integers which have at most k prime divisors. Then $\mathbb{N}(1)_p = \{p\}$ for every prime number p and so $d(\mathbb{N}(1)) = 0$. For $k > 1$ it holds $\mathbb{N}(k)_p \subset p\mathbb{N}(k - 1)$, and thus by induction we can prove that $d(\mathbb{N}(k)) = 0$ for every positive integer k.

In the paper [N1] the following result is proven:

Proposition. Let $\{p_n\}$ be such a sequence of different prime numbers that $\sum_{n=1}^{\infty} \frac{1}{p_n} = \infty$. Consider a set $S = \{s_n; n \in \mathbb{N}\}$. Put $q_n = \min\{p_k; p_k|s_n\}$ and $q_n = \infty$ if the number s_n is not divisible by any element form $\{p_n\}$. If $q_n \to \infty$ then $d(S) = 0$.

This statement follows from Theorem 3, considering that the set S_{p_n} is finite for every $n \in \mathbb{N}$.

Levy group

Suppose that for a permutation $g : \mathbb{N} \to \mathbb{N}$ the following properties

i) $\forall A \subseteq \mathbb{N}; \ A \in \mathcal{D} \implies g(A) \in \mathcal{D}$,

ii) $\forall A \in \mathcal{D}; \ d(g(A)) = d(A)$,

hold. Then we say that g *preserves the asymptotic density* (as usually $g(A) = \{g(a); a \in A\}$). Denote by G the set of all permutations $g : \mathbb{N} \to \mathbb{N}$ such that

$$\lim_{N \to \infty} \frac{1}{N} |\{j \leq N, g(j) > N\}| = 0.$$

This set is a group with respect to the composition low and it is called Lévy group, introduced in [LEV]. It can be proved easily that the permutations from G preserve the asymptotic density.

In the paper [OB], the following two theorems are proven:

iii) **Let γ be a finitely additive probability measure on $\mathcal{D}$ such that for every $g \in G$ and every $A \in \mathcal{D}$ it holds $\gamma(g(A)) = \gamma(A)$. Then $\gamma = d$.**

iv) **Let $A \in \mathcal{D}$. If for every $g \in G$ we have $d(A \ominus g(A)) = 0$ ($\ominus$ is the symmetric difference), then $d(A) = 1$ or $d(A) = 0$.**

In this part, we prove these results for a proper subgroup of G.
Denote by G_0 the set of all permutations $g : \mathbb{N} \to \mathbb{N}$ which fulfill the condition

$$\lim_{n \to \infty} \frac{g(n)}{n} = 1. \tag{1}$$

Proposition.

a) G_0 **is a subgroup of G.**

b) **The set $G \setminus G_0$ has the cardinality of the continuum.**

Proof

a) It is easy to prove that G_0 is a group. Thus it suffices to prove $G_0 \subset G$. Suppose that a permutation $g : \mathbb{N} \to \mathbb{N}$ does not belong to G. Then there exists $\varepsilon > 0$ and an infinite sequence $\{n_k\}$ of positive integers such that the number $j \in \mathbb{N}$, $j \le n_k$ verifying $g(j) > n_k$ exceeds the εn_k. Denote j_k such element from the set $\{1, ..., n_k\}$ such that $g(j_k) = \max\{g(j), 1 \le j \le n_k\}$. Then, between $g(j_k)$ and n_k, there are at least $\varepsilon n_k - 1$ numbers and so we have $g(j_k) \ge n_k + \varepsilon n_k \ge (1 + \varepsilon) j_k$. Thus, $\frac{g(j_k)}{j_k} \ge 1 + \varepsilon$. Clearly, $j_k \to \infty$, and so $g \notin G_0$.

b) Let $A = \{a_1 < a_2 < \ldots\}$ be an infinite subset of $\mathbb{N}$ such that $\lim_k \frac{a_{k+1}}{a_k} \to \infty$ and $d(A) = 0$. Put $A_1 = \{a_{2k-1}, k = 1, 2, \ldots\}$ and $A_2 = \{a_{2k}, k = 1, 2, \ldots\}$. Denote H the set of all permutations $g : \mathbb{N} \to \mathbb{N}$ such that $g(x) = x$ for $x \notin A$ and $g(A_1) = A_2, g(A_2) = A_1$. Easily, it can be proved that $H \subset G$. But for $g \in H$ and $a_k \in A$ we have $\frac{g(a_k)}{a_k} \ge \frac{a_{k+1}}{a_k}$ or $\frac{g(a_k)}{a_k} \le \frac{a_{k-1}}{a_k}$ thus $g \notin G_0$. Therefore $H \subset G \setminus G_0$. It is easy to see that H is uncountable. $\qquad \square$

Remark. Let $g : \mathbb{N} \to \mathbb{N}$ be an injective mapping. The set $\{g(1), \ldots, g(n)\}$ has n elements and so a little consideration shows that

$$\limsup_{n \to \infty} \frac{g(n)}{n} \ge 1.$$

Therefore the group G_0 consists of the permutations g with the lowest possible value of $\limsup_{n \to \infty} \frac{g(n)}{n}$.
Analogously as in [OB] this lemma will be crucial.

Lemma 1. Let $A, B \in \mathcal{D}$ be such that $A \cap B = \emptyset, d(A) = d(B) = \alpha \in (0, 1)$. **Then there exists such** $g \in G_0$ **that** $g(A) = B$.

Proof. Since $\alpha > 0$ the sets A, B are infinite. Denote
$A = \{a_1 < a_2 < \ldots\}, B = \{b_1 < b_2 < \ldots\}$
$\mathbb{N} \setminus A = \{a'_1 < a'_2 < \ldots\}, \mathbb{N} \setminus B = \{b'_1 < b'_2 < \ldots\}$.
Define the permutation $g : \mathbb{N} \to \mathbb{N}$ as follows $g(a_i) = b_i, g(a'_i) = b'_i$. Then $\frac{g(n)}{n} = \frac{a_i}{b_i}$ or $\frac{g(n)}{n} = \frac{a'_i}{b'_i}$, thus Theorem 1, page 9 yields that $g \in G_0$. $\qquad\square$

Theorem 4. Let γ be a finitely additive probability measure on $\mathcal{D}$ such that for every $g \in G_0$ and every $A \in \mathcal{D}$ it holds $\gamma(g(A)) = \gamma(A)$. Then $\gamma = d$.
d) Let $A \in \mathcal{D}$. If for every $g \in G_0$ we have

$$d(A \ominus g(A)) = 0 \qquad (2)$$

($\ominus$ **is the symmetric difference), then** $d(A) = 1$ or $d(A) = 0$.

Proof. The proof is a straightforward transcription of the proof from [O] c). Suppose that $A \in \mathcal{D}$ and $d(A) = \frac{1}{q}$ where $q \in \mathbb{N}$, $q > 1$. Due to Corollary 1 of Theorem 4 the set $\mathbb{N}$ can be decomposed $\mathbb{N} = A \cup A_1 \cup \cdots \cup A_{q-1}$ as a disjoint decomposition where the subsets A_j are elements of $\mathcal{D}$ with the density $\frac{1}{q}, j = 1, \ldots, q - 1$. From Lemma 1 we have that $A_j = g_j(A)$ for suitable permutations $g_j \in G_0, j = 1, \ldots, q - 1$. And so from the assumption of c) we deduce that $q \cdot \gamma(A) = 1$ thus $\gamma(A) = \frac{1}{q} = d(A)$. If now $B \in \mathcal{D}$ and $d(B)$ is a non-zero rational number then due to Corollary 1 of Theorem 1, page 9, the set B has a disjoint decomposition $B = B_1 \cup \cdots \cup B_p$ where $d(B_i) = \frac{1}{q}$. Thus also in this case we have $\gamma(B) = d(B)$. If $d(B) = 0$ then $d(\mathbb{N} \setminus B) = 1$ and so $\gamma(\mathbb{N} \setminus B) = 1$ thus $\gamma(B) = 0$. We have proved that $d(B) = \gamma(B)$ if $d(B)$ is rational. Suppose that $B \in \mathcal{D}$ and $d(B)$ is irrational. From Corollary 1 of Theorem 4, for any rational number $r > d(B)$ there exists a set B_r in $\mathcal{D}$ such that $B \subset B_r$ and $d(B_r) = r$. But in this case $\gamma(B_r) = r$. And so $\gamma(B) < r$; consequently $d(B) \geq \gamma(B)$. The same inequality for $\mathbb{N} \setminus B$ leads to $d(B) \leq \gamma(B)$, hence $d(B) = \gamma(B)$.
d) Suppose that for the set A from d) it holds that $0 < d(A) < 1$. Since the condition (2) holds also for $\mathbb{N} \setminus A$ we can suppose that $0 < d(A) \leq \frac{1}{2}$. Corollary 1 of Theorem 4 implies that there exists a set $A_1 \subset \mathbb{N} \setminus A$ with $d(A) = d(A_1)$. Therefore, from Lemma 1, we know that there exists a $g \in G_0$ such that $g(A) = A_1$. We have a contradiction with (2) because the sets $A, g(A) = A_1$ are disjointed. $\qquad\square$

Permutations which preserve having density

M. B. Nathanson and R. Parikh proved in [NP] the following result, which can be considered in certain sense as a definitive for the asymptotic density:

Theorem A. Let $f : \mathbb{N} \to \mathbb{N}$ be a one-to-one function such that if the set A of positive integers has asymptotic density, then the set $f(A)$ also has asymptotic density. Let

$$\lambda = d(f(\mathbb{N})).$$

Then for every $A \in \mathcal{D}$ **we have**

$$d(f(A)) = \lambda d(A).$$

Recently J. Bukor, L. Mišík and J. Toth obtained in [BMT] more general result which includes also other types of densities. This result will object of observations at the end of last chapter devoted to weight densities.

The permutations preserving the zero density

In the paper [N-P], it was proven that every permutation which preserves the property of "having the asymptotic density" preserves also the asymptotic density, thus i)⇒ ii) from the beginning of the previous part. Therefore, it makes no sense to study the permutation having only the property i). Now we shall study the permutations with more general property.

Lemma 1. Let $A \subset \mathbb{N}$ and $f : A \to \mathbb{N}$ be such a mapping that

$$\liminf_{A} \frac{f(n)}{n} > 0. \tag{1}$$

Then for every $S \subset A$ it holds

$$d(S) = 0 \Rightarrow d(f(S)) = 0. \tag{2}$$

Proof. The inequality (1) implies that for some $\alpha > 0$ we have $n \cdot \alpha < f(n), n \in \mathcal{A}$. This implies that for $x > 0$ we have $f(n) \leq x$ yields $n \cdot \alpha < x$. Thus for $S \subset \mathcal{A}$ we get $f(S)(x) \leq s(\frac{x}{\alpha})$. From this we immediately obtain (2). □

Corollary. Let $\varphi(n) = n \prod_{p|n}(1 - \frac{1}{p}), n \in \mathbb{N}$ be the Euler function. Then $d(\{\varphi(n); n \in \mathbb{N}\}) = 0$.

Proof: Denote $F = \{\varphi(n); n \in \mathbb{N}\}$. Then for arbitrary $r \in \mathbb{N}$ we can decompose the set F into two parts

$$F = \{\varphi(n); n \in \mathbb{N}(r)\} \cup \{\varphi(n); n \in \mathbb{N} \setminus \mathbb{N}(r)\} := F_1 \cup F_2.$$

Clearly, $F_2 \subset (2^{r-1})$. For $n \in \mathbb{N}(r)$ we have $\frac{\varphi(n)}{n} \geq \frac{1}{2^r} > 0$ and so considering that $d(\mathbb{N}(r)) = 0$, Lemma 1 implies $d(F_1) = 0$. We get $\overline{d}(F) \leq \frac{1}{2^{r-1}}$, since r is arbitrary, we obtain the assertion. □

If $f : \mathbb{N} \to \mathbb{N}$ fulfills the condition (2) that for every set $S \subset \mathbb{N}$, we say that f *preserves the zero density*.

For every set $S \subset \mathbb{N}$ it holds that $d(S) = 0$ if and only if $d(\mathbb{N} \setminus S) = 1$. From this we obtain immediately:

Lemma 2. Let $f : \mathbb{N} \to \mathbb{N}$ be a permutation. Then f preserves the zero density if and only if for every $R \subset \mathbb{N}$ it holds

$$d(R) = 1 \Rightarrow d(f(R)) = 1. \tag{3}$$

Theorem 5. Let $g : \mathbb{N} \to \mathbb{N}$ be such a permutation that there exists a set $A \subset \mathbb{N}$, $d(A) = 1 = d(g(A))$, and for every $S \subset A, d(S) = 0$ we have

$$\liminf_{S} \frac{g(n)}{n} > 0. \tag{4}$$

Then g preserves the zero density.

Proof. Let $R \subset \mathbb{N}$ and $d(R) = 1$. Then $d(R \cap A) = 1$. Thus $d(\mathbb{N} \setminus R \cap A) = 0$. From (4) and Lemma 1 we get $d(g(\mathbb{N} \setminus R \cap A)) = 0$. This yields $d(g(R \cap A)) = 1$, thus $d(g(R)) = 1$. The assertion follows from Lemma 2. $\qquad\square$

Example. Let $\mathbb{N} \setminus \{n^2, n \in \mathbb{N}\} = A \cup B$ and $\mathbb{N} \setminus \{n^3, n \in \mathbb{N}\} = C \cup D$, where $A = \{a_1 < a_2 < ...\}, B = \{b_1 < b_2 < ...\}, C = \{c_1 < c_2 < ...\}, D = \{d_1 < d_2 < ...\}$. Moreover $A \cap B = \emptyset = C \cap D$. Let us consider the permutation $g : \mathbb{N} \to \mathbb{N}$ where $g(n^2) = n^3, n \in \mathbb{N}$ and $g(a_k) = c_k, g(b_k) = d_k$. If we suppose that the sets A, B, C, D have positive asymptotic density, then g fulfills the assumption of Theorem 5. If $d(A) \neq d(C)$, then g preserves the zero density but does not preserve the asymptotic density.

Theorem 6. Let $g : \mathbb{N} \to \mathbb{N}$ be an injective mapping and $A \subset \mathbb{N}$, $A = \{a_1 < a_2 < ....\}$ an infinite set.

a) **If**
$$\lim_{n \to \infty} \frac{1}{a_n} \max\{g(a_j), j = 1, ..., n\} = 0, \tag{5}$$

then $d(A) = 0$.

b) **If**
$$\lim_{n \to \infty} \frac{g(a_n)}{a_n} = 0, \tag{6}$$

then $d(A) = 0$.

Proof. a) The values $g(a_j), j = 1, ..., n$ are different positive integers and so their maximum must be greater than $n - 1$. This implies
$$\frac{n}{a_n} \leq \frac{1}{a_n} \max\{g(a_j), j = 1, ..., n\}.$$

Now (5) implies $d(A) = 0$.

b) Put a_{k_n} such that $g(a_{k_n}) = \max\{g(a_j), j = 1, ..., n\}, n = 1, 2, ...$ Then
$$\frac{g(a_{k_n})}{a_n} \leq \frac{g(a_{k_n})}{a_{k_n}},$$

because $a_{k_n} \leq a_n$. The set $\{g(a_n), n = 1, 2, ...\}$ is infinite, and so $k_n \to \infty$ as $n \to \infty$. Therefore (6) implies (5). $\qquad\square$

As a corollary of Theorem 6 we obtain the following characterization of the sets of zero density in the terms of permutations.

Corollary. Let $A \subset \mathbb{N}$, $A = \{a_1 < a_2 < ....\}$ be an infinite set. Then $d(A) = 0$ if and only if there exists a permutation $g : \mathbb{N} \to \mathbb{N}$ fulfilling (6).

Proof. The sufficiency follows from Theorem 2. If $d(A) = 0$, then $\frac{n}{a_n} \to 0$ for $n \to \infty$. Put $B = \mathbb{N} \setminus \mathcal{A} = \{b_n, n = 1, 2, ...\}$. The permutation g given by $g(a_n) = 2n, g(b_n) = 2n + 1$, fulfills (6). $\qquad\square$

Statistical and ideal convergence

In the 1951 paper [FH], the following generalization of convergence is introduced: If $\{x_n\}$ is a sequence of real numbers, we say that a real value l is the *statistical limit* of this sequence if and only if for every $\varepsilon > 0$ the set $\{n; |x_n - l| \geq \varepsilon\}$ belongs to $\mathcal{D}$ and $d(\{n; |x_n - l| \geq \varepsilon\}) = 0$. This fact we shall denote $\lim -\text{stat } x_n = l$.

For the sequence $\{\Omega(n) - \omega(n)\}$ studied earlier on page 14 there holds

$$\lim -\text{stat } \frac{\Omega(n) - \omega(n)}{g(n)} = 0, \qquad (*)$$

for arbitrary sequence $\{g(n)\}$ such that $\lim_{n \to \infty} g(n) = \infty$.

We shall use the following symbol: for two subsets $A, B \subset \mathbb{N}$ we define $A \prec B$ if and only if $A \setminus A_1 \subset B$ for some finite set A_1. Clearly in this we have $\overline{d}(A) \leq \overline{d}(B)$.

And so $(*)$ follows immediately from the fact that for the arbitrary $\varepsilon > 0$ there holds

$$\left\{ n \in \mathbb{N}; \frac{\Omega(n) - \omega(n)}{g(n)} \geq \varepsilon \right\} \prec \bigcup_{k=N}^{\infty} E_k.$$

And from the equality (I) on page 17 it follows $\lim_{N \to \infty} d(\bigcup_{k=N}^{\infty} E_k) = 0$.

In 1980 Tibor Šalát in [Sal] proved the following result:

Proposition 1. A sequence $\{x_n\}$ of real numbers has statistical limit l if and only if for some set $A \in \mathcal{D}$, $d(A) = 1$ there holds $\lim_A x_n = l$.

Šalát, Kostyrko and Wilczynski in their paper [KSW] from 2001 proved a very general result which also includes statistical convergence. In the chapter, devoted to weight density, we prove the generalization of the results, a more general result (Proposition 2). A special case is the Proposition 1.

From Proposition 1, it can be derived

Oliviers theorem: If $\sum_{n=1}^{\infty} a_n < \infty, a_n \geq 0, n = 1, 2, \dots$ then there exists $A \in \mathcal{D}$ and $d(A) = 1$ that $\lim_A n a_n = 0$.

Proof. Let $B(\varepsilon) = \{n; na_n \geq \varepsilon\}$, for $\varepsilon > 0$. For $n \in B(\varepsilon)$ there holds $a_n \geq \frac{\varepsilon}{n}$ thus $\sum_{n \in B(\varepsilon)} \frac{1}{n} < \infty$ and so from Corollary 2 of Theorem 1, page 9, we have $d(B(\varepsilon)) = 0$ and the assertion follows from Proposition 1. $\qquad \square$

Now we introduce the generalization of convergence from [KSW].

Let $\mathcal{I}$ be a non empty system of subsets of $\mathbb{N}$. Then we say that $\mathcal{I}$ is an *admissible ideal* if and only if

a) For $A, B \in \mathcal{I}$ we have $A \cup B \in \mathcal{I}$.

b) If $A \in \mathcal{I}$ and $B \prec A$, then $B \in \mathcal{I}$.

For instance, the system I_d of all sets, having the asymptotic density 0, is an admissible ideal.

From the property b) it follows that every admissible ideal contains every finite set [iii].

[iii] In the paper [KSW], the admissible ideal is defined as a nonempty system of sets which contains all finite sets, contains a union of arbitrary two of its sets and with every set, it contains all it subsets. It is easy to see that this is equivalent to our definition.

We can define two types of convergence of the sequences or real numbers. Let $\mathcal{I}$ be an admissible ideal and $\{x_n\}$ be a sequence of real numbers. We say that a real value l is the $\mathcal{I}$ - *limit* of this sequence if and only if every $\varepsilon > 0$ the set $\{n; |x_n - l| \geq \varepsilon\}$ belongs to $\mathcal{I}$, we write in short $\mathcal{I} - \lim x_n = l$.

We say that the sequence $\{x_n\}$ has $\mathcal{I}^*$ - *limit* l if and only if for some set $A \subset \mathbb{N}$ that $\mathbb{N} \setminus A \in \mathcal{I}$ there holds $\lim_A x_n = l$, shortly $\mathcal{I}^* - \lim x_n = l$.

Proposition 1 says that $\mathcal{I}_d - \lim x_n = l \iff \mathcal{I}_d^* - \lim x_n = l$. We can see immediately that for arbitrary admissible ideal there holds $\mathcal{I}^* - \lim x_n = l \implies \mathcal{I} - \lim x_n = l$. In the paper [KSW] the sufficient and necessary condition for the opposite implication and thus for the equivalence of both convergence is given as follows:

Proposition 2. Let $\mathcal{I}$ be an admissible ideal, then the following conditions are equivalent:

(a) **For every sequence of real numbers $\{x_n\}$ and l - real number there holds $\mathcal{I} - \lim x_n = l \iff \mathcal{I}^* - \lim x_n = l$.**

(b) **For every sequence of sets $\{B_k\}$ from $\mathcal{I}$ there exists a set $B \in \mathcal{I}$ that $B_k \prec B$, for $k = 1, 2, ...$**

Proof.

(b)$\implies$(a).

Let $\mathcal{I} - \lim x_n = l$. Let us denote $B_k = \{n; |x_n - l| \geq \frac{1}{k}\}$, $k = 1, 2, ...$ Then from (b) we get that there exists a set $B \in \mathcal{I}$ that $B_k \prec B, k = 1, 2, ...$ Put $A = \mathbb{N} \setminus B$. Clearly, $A \prec \mathbb{N} \setminus B_k, k = 1, 2, ...$, and so for $k = 1, 2, ...$ there exists n_k that for $n \in A$ and $n > n_k$ we have $|x_n - l| < \frac{1}{k}$ therefore $\mathcal{I}^* - \lim x_n = l$.

(a)$\implies$(b).

Let us define the sequence $\{x_n\}$ as follows: If $n \in \cup_{k=1}^{\infty} B_k$, then $x_n = \frac{1}{s}$ where $s = \min\{k; n \in B_k\}$, $x_n = 0$ otherwise. For $\varepsilon > 0$ we have $\{n; |x_n| \geq \varepsilon\} \subset \cup_{k \leq \frac{1}{\varepsilon}} B_k$, thus $\{n; |x_n| \geq \varepsilon\}$ belongs to $\mathcal{I}$, and so $\mathcal{I} - \lim x_n = 0$. From (a) we obtain that there exists $B \in \mathcal{I}$ that for $A = \mathbb{N} \setminus B$ we have $\lim_A x_n = 0$, this yields where $B_k \prec B, k = 1, 2, ...$ $\square$

Infinite series. There is also a connection between the ideal and the convergence of infinite series with non negative elements.

A non negative function m defined on the system of sets of positive integers is called *submeasure* if and only if

a) $m(A \cup B) \leq m(A) + m(B)$
   and

b) $A \subset B \implies m(A) \leq m(B)$
   for all sets of positive integers A, B.

   A submeasure m is called *compact submeasure* if and only if

c) for every $\varepsilon > 0$ there exists a finite decomposition $\mathbb{N} = A_1 \cup ... \cup A_j$ such that for $i = 1, ..., j$ we have $m(A_i) < \varepsilon$.

The last condition provides that for a compact submeasure m we have $m(\{a\}) = 0$ for every $a \in \mathbb{N}$, thus $m(F) = 0$ for every finite set $F \subset \mathbb{N}$. This yields that the system $I_m = \{A \subset \mathbb{N}; m(A) = 0\}$ forms an admissible ideal.

The following property is a generalization of the result from [EK]:

Theorem: Let m be a compact submeasure. Consider the sequence of non negative real numbers $\{a_n\}$. Then $\sum_{n=1}^{\infty} a_n < \infty$ if and only if $\sum_{n \in B} a_n < \infty$ for every $B \in I_m$.

Proof: The implication $\Rightarrow$ is evident.

Assume that $\sum_{n=1}^{\infty} a_n = \infty$, we construct a set B such that $m(B) = 0$ and $\sum_B a_n = \infty$.

Denote $S(A) = \sum_A a_n$, for $A \subset \mathbb{N}$. From the condition c) we obtain that there exists a decomposition

$$\mathbb{N} = A_1^{(1)} \cup ... \cup A_k^{(1)}$$

that $m(A_i^{(1)}) < 1, i = 1, ..., k$. From the divergence of $\sum_{n=1}^{\infty} a_n$ we deduce that for suitable index i_0 we have $S(A_{i_0}^{(1)}) = \infty$. Put $A^{(1)} = A_{i_0}^{(1)}$. Again the condition c) implies the existence of the decomposition

$$\mathbb{N} = A_1^{(2)} \cup ... \cup A_l^{(2)}$$

that $m(A_i^{(2)}) < \frac{1}{2}, i = 1, ..., l$. This yields

$$A^{(1)} = A^{(1)} \cap A_1^{(2)} \cup ... \cup A^{(1)} \cap A_l^{(2)}$$

and from the condition $S(A^{(1)}) = \infty$ we obtain that for a suitable i_1 there holds $S(A_{i_1}^{(2)} \cap A^{(1)}) = \infty$. Put $A^{(2)} = A_{i_1}^{(2)} \cap A^{(1)}$. By repeating this procedure, we construct non increasing sequence of the sets

$$A^{(1)} \supset A^{(2)} \supset ... \supset A^{(n)} \supset ...$$

that

$$m(A^{(n)}) < \frac{1}{n} \qquad (i)$$

and

$$S(A^{(n)}) = \infty \qquad (ii)$$

for $n = 1, 2, ...$

From (ii) it follows that there exists an increasing sequence of positive integers $\{j_k\}$ that

$$S(A^{(1)} \cap \{1, ..., j_1\}) > 1$$

and

$$S(A^{(n)} \cap \{j_{n-1} + 1, ..., j_n\}) > 1$$

for $n > 1$. Denote $B_1 = A^{(1)} \cap \{1, ..., j_1\}$, $B_n = A^{(n)} \cap \{j_{n-1} + 1, ..., j_n\}, n > 1$. Put $B = \cup_{n=1}^{\infty} B_n$. Clearly $S(B) = \infty$. The sets $B_n, n = 1, 2, ...$ are finite, therefore

$$m(B) \leq m(B_1) + ... + m(B_n) + m(\cup_{k=n+1}^{\infty} B_k) = m(\cup_{k=n+1}^{\infty} B_k).$$

Considering that $\cup_{k=n+1}^{\infty} B_k \subset A^{(n+1)}$ we get from (i) that $m(B) \leq \frac{1}{n+1}, n = 1, 2, ...$ For $n \to \infty$ we obtain $m(B) = 0$. $\qquad \square$

Probability on the finite sets

The form of ideal convergence gives the possibility to use Chebyshev inequality from the elementary theory of probability. For this statement, we refer also to the monograph [Re].

Let $N \in \mathbb{N}$. We can consider the set function $d_N : P(N) \to <0, 1>$, where $d_N(A) = \frac{A(N)}{N}$, for $A \subset \mathbb{N}$. This function is an atomic probability measure, with a finite set of atoms $\{1, 2, ..., N\}$. Every arithmetic function, f can be considered as random variable with the mean value

$$E_N(f) = \frac{1}{N} \sum_{n=1}^{N} f(n)$$

and discrepancy

$$D_N^2(f) = \frac{1}{N} \sum_{n=1}^{N} (f(n) - E_N)^2 = E_N(f^2) - E_N(f)^2.$$

From the Chebyshev inequality, we obtain for $\varepsilon > 0$

$$d_N(\{n; |f(n) - E_N(f)| \geq \varepsilon\}) \leq \frac{D_N^2(f)}{\varepsilon^2}. \qquad (a)$$

If there exists a proper limit $\lim_{N \to \infty} E_N(f) := E(f)$ then $E(f)$ is called *mean value* of f and we say that f has the mean value. For instance, the asymptotic density of a given set is the mean value of its indicator function.

Suppose now that f has a mean value. Then for N positive integer we have

$$|f(n) - E(f)| \leq |f(n) - E_N(f)| + |E_N(f) - E(f)|$$

and so for $\varepsilon > 0$ it holds

$$\{n; |f(n) - E(f)| \geq \varepsilon\} \subset \left\{n; |f(n) - E_N(f)| \geq \frac{\varepsilon}{2}\right\} \cup \left\{n; |E(f) - E_N(f)| \geq \frac{\varepsilon}{2}\right\}$$

therefore

$$d_N(\{n; |f(n) - E(f)| \geq \varepsilon\}) \leq$$
$$\leq d_N\left(\left\{n; |f(n) - E_N(f)| \geq \frac{\varepsilon}{2}\right\}\right) + d_N\left(\left\{n; |E(f) - E_N(f)| \geq \frac{\varepsilon}{2}\right\}\right)$$

From(a) we get

$$d_N(\{n; |f(n) - E(f)| \geq \varepsilon\}) \leq \frac{4D_N^2(f)}{\varepsilon^2} + d_N\left(\left\{n; |E(f) - E_N(f)| \geq \frac{\varepsilon}{2}\right\}\right). \qquad (b)$$

Now we can prove the Chebyshev inequality for the upper asymptotic density:

Proposition A. Let f be such an arithmetic function, that f and f^2 have mean value. Then for every $\varepsilon > 0$ there holds

$$\overline{d}(\{n; |f(n) - E(f)| \geq \varepsilon\}) \leq \frac{4D^2(f)}{\varepsilon^2}$$

where $D^2(f) = E(f^2) - E(f)^2$.

Proof. The assertion follows immediately from (b) if we consider that the set $\left\{n; |E(f) - E_N(f)| \geq \frac{\varepsilon}{2}\right\}$ is finite. $\square$

The value $D^2(f) = E(f^2) - E(f)^2$ is called *dispersion* of f.

Using Proposition 1 and Proposition A we obtain:

Proposition B. a) Let f be such an arithmetic function, that f and f^2 have mean value. If $D^2(f) = 0$, then there exists a set $A \in \mathcal{D}$ that $d(A) = 1$ and $\lim_A f(n) = E(f)$. b) If f is bounded and there exists a set $A \in \mathcal{D}$ that $d(A) = 1$ and $\lim_A f(n) = E(f)$ then $D^2(f) = 0$.

If we have two arithmetic functions, f, g that we can consider as the random variables which, with respect to probability, measure d_N. If $D_N^2(f) > 0, D_N^2(g) > 0$ then their regress line is

$$y = a_N x + b_N$$

where

$$a_N = \frac{E_N(fg) - E_N(f)E_N(g)}{D_N^2(f)}, \quad b_N = E_N(g) - a_N E_N(f),$$

and correlation coefficient

$$\rho_N(f, g) = \frac{|E_N(fg) - E_N(f)E_N(g)|}{D_N^2(f)D_N^2(g)}.$$

Put $h = a_N f + b_N - g$. Using a simple calculation we can prove

$$E_N(h) = 0, \quad D_N^2(h) = (1 - \rho_N^2(f, g))(D_N^2(g)). \tag{c}$$

Thus $\rho_N(f, g) = 1$ yields $0 = h(n) = a_N f(n) + b_N - g(n)$ for $n = 1, ..., N$. Using Proposition 1, Proposition A and Proposition B we can extend this in the following way:

Proposition C. Let f, g be such arithmetic functions that f, f^2, g, g^2, fg have mean value and $D_N^2(f) > 0, D_N^2(g) > 0, D^2(f) > 0, D^2(g) > 0$. Put $\rho(f, g) = \lim_{N \to \infty} \rho_N(f, g)$, $a = \lim_{N \to \infty} a_N, b = \lim_{N \to \infty} b_N$. Then

$$\overline{d}(\{n; |af(n) + b - g(n)| \geq \varepsilon\}) \leq \frac{4(1 - \rho^2(f, g))(D^2(g))}{\varepsilon^2}.$$

If moreover $\rho(f, g) = 1$ then there exists such $A \in \mathcal{D}$ that $d(A) = 1$ and $\lim_A af(n) + b - g(n) = 0$.

As an example on which Proposition C can be applied, we can consider the almost periodic functions, also called the Besicovitch functions, introduced in 1954 in [B] as follows: an arithmetic function, f is called *almost periodic* if and only if, for the arbitrary $\varepsilon > 0$, there exists a periodic function f_ε that

$$\limsup_{N \to \infty} \frac{1}{N} \sum_{n=1}^{N} |f(n) - f_\varepsilon(n)| < \varepsilon.$$

It is easy to prove that every bounded Besicovitch function f has a mean value, and if f, g are bounded Besicovitch functions then the product fg is also a bounded Besicovitch function. For the survey of Besicovitch functions we refer also to [P].

A special case of almost periodic functions are the arithmetic functions, satisfying a certain condition of continuity which is a generalization of $p-$ adic continuity. An arithmetic function, is called *polyadicly continuous* if and only if for every $\varepsilon > 0$ there exists $m \in \mathbb{N}$ that

$$n_1 \equiv n_2 \pmod{m} \Rightarrow |f(n_1) - f(n_2)| < \varepsilon.$$

Every polyadicly continuous arithmetic function can be uniformly approximated by periodic functions, thus it is almost periodic.

These types of functions are studied in [N], [N1], because they can be extended to the uniformly continuous functions on the ring of polyadic integers. For the survey on polyadic integers we refer also to the monograph [P]. As an example of polyadicly continuous function, we can take the function (see [P])

$$\frac{\sigma(n)\varphi(n)}{n^2} = \prod_{p|n}\left(1 - \frac{1}{p^{\alpha_p(n)+1}}\right), n \in \mathbb{N},$$

where $\alpha_p(n) = \max\{k = 0, 1, ...; p^k|n\}$.

For every polyadicly continuous arithmetic function, f there holds:

If for some $n_0 \in \mathbb{N}$ holds $|f(n_0)| > 0$ then there exists a constant $c > 0$ and arithmetic progression $n_0 + (m)$ that for $n \in n_0 + (m)$ we have $|f(n)| > c$.

Thus we get immediately

a) $\lim -\text{stat} f(n) = L$ **if and only if $f(n) = L, n \in \mathbb{N}$.**

b) $E(|f|) = 0$ **if and only if $f(n) = 0, n \in \mathbb{N}$.**

And so

c) $D^2(f) = 0$ **if and only if f is the constant function.**

d) **If f, g are non constant polyadic continuous arithmetic functions, then $\rho(f, g) = 1$ if and only if $f = Ag + B$, where A, B are constants.**

Uniform distribution modulo 1

The notion of uniformly distributed sequences was introduced in 1916 by Hermann Weyl, see [WEY]. Suppose that $\{x_n\}$ is a sequence of elements of interval $< 0, 1)$. Let $I =< a, b), a < b$ be a subinterval of $< 0, 1)$. Denote $A(\{x_n\}, I) = \{n \in \mathbb{N}; x_n \in I\}$. Then the sequence $\{x_n\}$ is called *uniformly distributed* if and only if $A(\{x_n\}, I) \in \mathcal{D}$, and $d(A(\{x_n\}, I)) = b - a$ for every subinterval $I \subset < 0, 1)$. In the other words, this can be expressed as follows:

$$\lim_{N \to \infty} \frac{1}{N} \sum_{n=1}^{N} \chi_I(x_n) = |I|,$$

where χ_I is the indicator function of I, and $|I|$ is the length of I. Every continuous real valued function f defined on the interval $< 0,1 >$ can be, for arbitrary $\varepsilon > 0$, approximated by the step functions f_1, f_2 in such a way that $f_1 \leq f \leq f_2$ and $\int_0^1 (f_2 - f_1) < \varepsilon$ and, vice-versa, every indicator function of interval χ_I can be approximated by continuous functions g_1, g_2, so that $g_1 \leq \chi_I \leq g_2$ and $\int_0^1 (g_2 - g_1) < \varepsilon$. Moreover, every step function is a linear combination of the indicator functions of intervals. Using this fact we can prove the following criterion, well known as

Weyl's criterion. **A sequence $\{x_n\}$ of elements of interval $< 0,1)$ is uniformly distributed if and only if for every real valued continuous function defined on $< 0,1 >$ it holds**

$$\lim_{N \to \infty} \frac{1}{N} \sum_{n=1}^{N} f(x_n) = \int_0^1 f(x) dx.$$

Every real valued function continuous on closed interval with the same value in the endpoints can be uniformly approximated by a trigonometric polynomial, and so we obtain the trigonometric form of Weyl's criterion :

A sequence $\{x_n\}$ of elements of interval $< 0,1)$ is uniformly distributed if and only if for every non zero integer h it holds

$$\lim_{N \to \infty} \frac{1}{N} \sum_{n=1}^{N} e^{2\pi i h x_n} = 0.$$

From the trigonometric form of Weyl's criterion, we obtain that for an irrational number α and arbitrary real number β the sequence of fractional parts $\{\{n\alpha + \beta\}\}$ is uniformly distributed. Using this result, Oto Strauch proved the following statement in 1984:

Proposition. If $I \subset < 0,1)$ is an interval of positive length and α is an irrational number, then the set $A(\{\{n\alpha\}\}, I)$ has infinite intersection with arbitrary arithmetic progression.

Proof. For $m \in \mathbb{N}, r \in \mathbb{Z}$ the sequence $\{\{(nm + r)\alpha\}\}$ is uniformly distributed, thus $d(A(\{\{(nm + r)\alpha\}, I)) = |I| > 0$, and so the set $A(\{\{(nm + r)\alpha\}, I)$ is infinite therefore $n_i m + r \in A(\{n\alpha\}, I)$ for some infinite sequence of positive integers $\{n_i\}$ [iv]. $\qquad\square$

Distribution of the values of the additive functions

An arithmetic function, h is called *additive* if and only if for relatively primes positive integers n_1, n_2 there holds $h(n_1 n_2) = h(n_1) + h(n_2)$. An additive arithmetic function, f is called *strong additive* if for every prime p and α positive integer we have $f(p^\alpha) = f(p)$. Pal Erdös proved the following results on distribution of values of such functions on real line:

Theorem A: Let f be a non-negative strong additive arithmetic function, such as for different primes p_1, p_2 we have $f(p_1) \neq f(p_2)$ and the infinite series $\sum_{p-prime} \frac{f(p)}{p}$ converges. Then for every interval I, there holds $A(\{f(n)\}, I) \in \mathcal{D}$. Moreover, in this case, the function $g(x) = d(A(\{f(n)\}, < -\infty, x))$ is continuous on real line [v].

[iv] In the original paper, Weyl studied the sequence of fractional parts $\{\{x_n\}\}$ for arbitrary sequence of real numbers. Therefore this notion is called uniform distribution modulo 1.

[v] By application Theorem A to the function $f(n) = -\ln \frac{\varphi(n)}{n}, n \in \mathbb{N}$ we get that the sequence $\{\frac{\varphi(n)}{n}\}$, φ is the Euler function, has a continuous asymptotic distribution function, (This notion is defined on page 57).

Theorem B: **Let h be an non negative additive arithmetic function, such that for two different primes p_1, p_2 we have $h(p_1) \neq h(p_2)$ and the infinite series $\sum_{p-prime} \frac{h(p)}{p}$ converges. Then for every interval I the set $A(\{h(n)\}, I)$ belongs to $\mathcal{D}$.**

We give the proof from original paper [Er1]. We start with following two statements:

Proposition I: **Let f be an strong - additive arithmetic function with non negative values such that for every two different primes p_1, p_2 there holds $f(p_1) \neq f(p_2)$. Suppose that the infinite series $\sum_{p-prime} \frac{f(p)}{p}$ converges. Denote $f_N(n) = \sum_{p \leq N} f(p), n, N \in \mathbb{N}$. Then for every $\delta > 0$ we have**

$$\lim_{N \to \infty} \overline{d}(\{m; f(m) - f_N(m) > \delta\}) = 0.$$

Proof: Let δ be fixed. Put $A_N = \{m; f(m) - f_N(m) > \delta\}, N \in \mathbb{N}$. We shall estimate the value $A_N(n), N, n \in \mathbb{N}$.

By a calculation we get

$$\sum_{m=1}^{n} f(m) - f_N(m) = \sum_{N < p \leq n} f(p) \left[\frac{n}{p}\right] = n \sum_{N < p \leq n} \frac{f(p)}{p} + O(P(n))$$

where P is the set of all primes. $A_N(n)$ is the number of the summands greater than δ, and so this value does not exceed

$$\frac{n}{\delta} \sum_{N < p \leq n} \frac{f(p)}{p} + O(P(n)).$$

Since $d(P) = 0$ we get $\overline{d}(A_N) \leq \frac{1}{\delta} \sum_{N < p} \frac{f(p)}{p}$. The proof is complete. $\qquad\square$

Proposition II: **Let f be an strong - additive arithmetic function such that for every two different primes p_1, p_2 there holds $f(p_1) \neq f(p_2)$. Then for every $\varepsilon > 0$ there exists $\delta > 0$ that for every interval I we have**

$$|I| < \delta \implies \overline{d}(A(\{f(n)\}, I)) < \varepsilon.$$

Proof: Let $q_1, ..., q_s$ be a sequence of consecutive primes. Put $\delta = \min\{|f(q_i) - f(q_j)|; i \neq j\}$. Let I be an interval and $|I| < \delta$. Denote $A := A(\{f(n)\}, I)$. Then denote

$$A \subset \left(\mathbb{N} \setminus \bigcup_{j=1}^{s}(q_j)\right) \cup \left(A \cap \left(\bigcup_{j=1}^{s}(q_j) \setminus \bigcup_{j=1}^{s}(q_j^2)\right)\right) \cup \bigcup_{j=1}^{s}(q_j^2).$$

Thus Theorem 1, page 12, implies

$$\overline{d}(A) \leq \prod_{j=1}^{s}\left(1 - \frac{1}{q_j}\right) + \overline{d}(A_1) + 1 - \prod_{j=1}^{s}\left(1 - \frac{1}{q_j^2}\right),$$

where $A_1 = \left(A \cap \left(\bigcup_{j=1}^{s}(q_j) \setminus \bigcup_{j=1}^{s}(q_j^2)\right)\right)$. Let $\varepsilon > 0$. We can chose the primes $q_1, ..., q_s$ such that the first and third summands in the last inequality are smaller than $\frac{\varepsilon}{3}$. Thus we have to estimate only $\overline{d}(A_1)$.

Each positive integer $m \in A_1$ is divisible by some $q_j, 1 \leq j \leq s$. We prove that the numbers $\frac{m}{q_j}, m \in A_1, q_j | m$ are different. Let

$$\frac{m_1}{q_j} = \frac{m_2}{q_i}, m_1, m_2 \in A_1, m_1 \neq m_2,$$

then

$$f\left(\frac{m_1}{q_j}\right) = f\left(\frac{m_2}{q_i}\right).$$

Therefore

$$f(m_1) - f(q_j) = f(m_2) - f(q_i) \implies f(m_1) - f(m_2) = f(q_i) - f(q_j).$$

This is a contradiction because $|f(m_1) - f(m_2)| < \delta$ and $|f(q_i) - f(q_j)| > \delta$. Hence if $n \in \mathbb{N}$ and $m_1, ..., m_k$ are all elements of A_1 not exceeding n then the numbers $\frac{m_j}{q_{j'}}, j = 1, ..., k$ are different elements of interval $< 1, \frac{n}{q_1} >$ and so $k \leq \frac{n}{q_1}$. This yields $A_1(n) \leq \frac{n}{q_1}$, hence $\overline{d}(A_1) \leq \frac{1}{q_1}$. If we chose q_1 such that $\frac{1}{q_1} \leq \frac{\varepsilon}{3}$ the assertion follows.   □

Proof of Theorem A: Let $f_N, N \in \mathbb{N}$ be the functions defined in Proposition I. These functions are periodic, thus for every interval I there holds $A(\{f_N(n)\}, I) \in \mathcal{D}$.

It suffices to prove that the set $A(\{f(n)\}, < x, \infty))$ belongs to $\mathcal{D}$ for every real number x. For the proof, we shall use the property ix) on the page 12. Clearly $A(\{f_N(n)\}, < x, \infty)) \subset A(\{f(n)\}, < x, \infty))$ and

$$A(\{f(n)\}, < x, \infty)) \setminus A(\{f_N(n)\}, < x, \infty)) = \{n \in \mathbb{N}; f_N(n) < x \wedge f(n) \geq x\}.$$

For an arbitrary positive δ we have

$$\{n \in \mathbb{N}; f_N(n) < x \wedge f(n) \geq x\} \subset A(\{f(n)\}, < x, x + \delta)) \cup \{n; f(n) - f_N(n) > \delta\}.$$

If $\varepsilon > 0$ then from Proposition II we have that there exists $\delta > 0$ that $\overline{d}(A(\{f(n)\}, < x, x + \delta))) < \frac{\varepsilon}{2}$ and for this δ we can find, by Proposition I, such N_0 that $\overline{d}(\{n; f(n) - f_N(n) > \delta\}) < \frac{\varepsilon}{2}$. Hence for this N_0 we have $\overline{d}(A(\{f(n)\}, < x, \infty)) \setminus A(\{f_N(n)\}, < x, \infty))) < \varepsilon$. Considering that $A(\{f_N(n)\}, < x, \infty)) \in \mathcal{D}$ the assertion follows from ix) page 12. (The continuity of g follows immediately from proposition II.)   □

Proof of Theorem B: Denote $f(n) = \sum_{p|n} h(p)$. Then for square free integer n there holds $f(n) = h(n)$.

Let M be the set of all positive integers with all exponents in canonical representation greater than 1. Assume that $q \in M, q = q_1^{\alpha_1}...q_k^{\alpha_k}$. Consider the set

$$F(q) = F(q_1, ..., q_k) = \mathbb{N} \setminus \left((q_1) \cup ... \cup (q_k) \cup \bigcup_{p \neq q_j} (p^2)\right).$$

as on page 16. If a is an arbitrary periodic arithmetic function with the period m, then for every interval I the set $\{n \in F(q); a(n) \in I\}$ is the disjoint union of the sets of the form $r + (m) \cap F(q)$ and all these sets belong to $\mathcal{D}$, and so $\{n \in F(q); a(n) \in I\}$ belongs to $\mathcal{D}$.

Denote $f(n) = \sum_{p|n} h(p)$. Then a for square free integer n, there holds $f(n) = h(n)$ and so, analogously to Proposition III, it can be proved that the set $\{n \in F(q); f(n) \in I\}$ belongs to $\mathcal{D}$ for each $q \in M$.

The set of positive integers can be represented as disjoint decomposition $\mathbb{N} = Q_2 \cup \bigcup_{q \in M} qF(q)$. Hence

$$A(\{h(n)\}, I) = \{n \in Q_2; f(n) \in I\} \cup \bigcup_{q \in M} \{n \in qF(q); h(n) \in I\}.$$

Clearly $\{n \in qF(q); h(n) \in I\} = q\{n \in F(q); f(n) \in I_q\}$ where $I_q = \{x - h(q); x \in I\}$. The function f is strongly additive, thus Proposition III guarantees that $\{n \in F(q); f(n) \in I_q\}$ belongs to $\mathcal{D}$. The infinite series $\sum_{q \in M} \frac{1}{q}$ converges and so the assertion follows from Proposition I page 15. $\qquad\square$

The extension of asymptotic density

The notion of the limit of convergent sequences can be extended via well known Hahn - Banach theorem to a linear function defined on the linear space of all bounded sequences of real numbers. This generalized limit is called the Banach limit (see [BAN]). Dorothy Maharam in the paper [M] expands the asymptotic density on the system of all subsets of $\mathbb{N}$ as the Banach limit of the value $\frac{A(N)}{N}$, $N \to \infty$. This is an example of finitely additive probability measure on the system of all subsets of $\mathbb{N}$ whose value is 0 for finite sets. This type of set functions has been studied in the paper [S-T]. In this part, we quote the results from this paper which characterize the connection between the richness of the set and its measure.

Let $\gamma : \mathcal{P}(\mathbb{N}) \to <0,1>$ be a finitely additive probability measure, such that $\gamma(S) = d(S)$ for every $S \in \mathcal{D}$, then we say that γ is *extension of asymptotic density*.

Theorem A. Let γ be extension of asymptotic density. Then for every two infinite sets $A, B \subset \mathbb{N}$ there holds

$$\lim_{N \to \infty} \frac{A(N)}{B(N)} = 1 \implies \gamma(A) = \gamma(B).$$

We start the proof by following the simpler case:

Lemma I. Let γ be extension of asymptotic density. Then for every two infinite disjoint sets $A, B \subset \mathbb{N}$ there holds

$$\lim_{N \to \infty} \frac{A(N)}{B(N)} = 1 \implies \gamma(A) = \gamma(B).$$

Proof: Let $C \subset \mathbb{N}$ be such set that $A \cap C = \emptyset = B \cap C$ and $A \cup C, B \cup C \in \mathcal{D}$ and $d(A \cup C) = d(B \cup C)$. Then from the assumption we obtain

$$\gamma(A \cup C) = \gamma(B \cup C)$$

thus

$$\gamma(A) = \gamma(B).$$

Thus it suffices to construct the set C with prescribed properties. Put $D = (A \cup B)$ and $E = \mathbb{N} \setminus D$. If E is a finite set the we obtain immediately that $A, B \in \mathcal{D}$ and $d(A) = d(B) = \frac{1}{2}$. Let $E = \{e_1 < ... < e_n < ...\}$ be an infinite set. Let us put $C = \{e_{2k+1}; k = 0, 1, ...\}$. From the assumption we have that for $\varepsilon > 0$ there exists N_0 that for $N > N_0$ we have

$$(1 - \varepsilon)B(N) \leq A(N) \leq (1 + \varepsilon)B(N) \qquad (a)$$

and

$$(1 - \varepsilon)A(N) \leq B(N) \leq (1 + \varepsilon)A(N). \qquad (b)$$

From (a) it follows

$$-\varepsilon B(N) \leq A(N) - B(N) \leq \varepsilon B(N). \qquad (c)$$

Clearly, $A(N) - B(N) = 2A(N) + E(N) - N$. We see immediately that $0 \leq 2C(N) - E(N) \leq 1$ thus $E(N) = 2C(N) + \rho_N$ where $0 \leq \rho_N \leq 1$. Thus from (c) we obtain

$$-\varepsilon \leq \frac{2A(N) + 2C(N) + \rho_N}{N} - 1 \leq \varepsilon$$

for $N > N_0$, and so $d(A \cup C) = \frac{1}{2}$. Analogously we can derive from (b) that $d(B \cup C) = \frac{1}{2}$. $\square$

Corollary I. Let γ be the extension of asymptotic density. If $A, B \subset \mathbb{N}$ are disjoint set such that $A(N) - B(N)$ is bounded then $\gamma(A) = \gamma(B)$.

Corollary II. Let γ be extension of asymptotic density. Consider $A = \{a_1 < a_2 < ...\}$ an infinite set and m positive integer. Put $A_j = \{a_{mr+j}; r = 0, 1, ...\}, j = 0, ..., m - 1$. Then $\gamma(A_j) = \frac{\gamma(A)}{m}$.

The assertion follows directly from the fact that for $0 \leq i, j m - 1$ the sequence $A_j(N) - A_i(N)$ is bounded.

For the proof of Theorem A, we shall use the following easy lemma on the limits of real sequences

Lemma II. Let $\{a_n\}, \{b_n\}, \{c_n\}, \{d_n\}$ be the sequences of positive real numbers such that $\frac{a_n}{b_n} \to 1, \frac{c_n}{d_n} \to 1, n \to \infty, c_n > d_n, n = 1, 2, ...$ and the value $\frac{c_n + d_n}{c_n - d_n}$ is bounded for $n = 1, 2, ...$ Then

$$\lim_{n \to \infty} \frac{a_n - b_n}{c_n - d_n} = 1.$$

This statement can be verified by standard calculation.

Proof of Theorem A: Put $D = A \cap B$. If D is a finite set then by applying Lemma I to the sets $A \setminus D, B$, we obtain the assertion. Suppose that $D = \{d_1 < d_2 < ....\}$ is an infinite set. Put $D_1 = \{d_{2k-1}, k = 1, 2, ...\}$ and $D_2 = \{d_{2k}, k = 1, 2, ...\}$. The value $D_1(N) - D_2(N)$ is bounded and so by Corollary we have $\gamma(D_1) = \gamma(D_2)$. Denote $A^* = A \setminus D_1, B^* = A \setminus D_2$. Easy can be verified that $A^* \cap B^* = \emptyset$. Clearly ,

$$\frac{A^*(N)}{B^*(N)} = \frac{A(N) - D_1(N)}{B(N) - D_2(N)}.$$

It holds $B(N) - D_2(N) \geq \frac{B(N)}{2}$, $B(N) + D_2(N) \leq 2B(N)$. Thus $\frac{B(N)+D_2(N)}{B(N)-D_2(N)} \leq 4$. Considering now that $\frac{D_1(N)}{D_2(N)} \to 1$ we obtain from Lemma II that

$$\lim_{N\to\infty} \frac{A^*(N)}{B^*(N)} = 1$$

thus $\gamma(A^*) = \gamma(B^*)$, this yields $\gamma(A) = \gamma(B)$. $\qquad \square$

Corollary III. Let γ be an extension of asymptotic density. If $A, B \subset \mathbb{N}$ are such that $A(N) - B(N)$ is bounded then $\gamma(A) = \gamma(B)$.

Corollary IV. Let γ be an extension of asymptotic density. For every $A \subset \mathbb{N}$ we have $\gamma(A+1) = \gamma(A)$.

Theorem B. Let γ be an extension of asymptotic density. Then for every two infinite sets $A, B \subset \mathbb{N}$ and a positive real number t it holds

$$\lim_{N\to\infty} \frac{A(N)}{B(N)} = t \implies \gamma(A) = t\gamma(B).$$

Proof: If $t = 0$ then $d(A) = 0$ and the assertion holds. Suppose that $t = \frac{p}{q} > 0$ is rational. Let $A = \{a_1 < a_2...\}$ and $B = \{b_1 < b_2...\}$. Define the sets $A^* = \{a_{pn}; n \in \mathbb{N}\}$ and $B^* = \{b_{qn}; n \in \mathbb{N}\}$. Then $\frac{A^*(N)}{A(N)} \to \frac{1}{p}$ and $\frac{B^*(N)}{B(N)} \to \frac{1}{q}$ for $N \to \infty$ and so

$$\lim_{N\to\infty} \frac{A^*(N)}{B^*(N)} = 1.$$

Theorem A implies $\gamma(A^*) = \gamma(B^*)$. From Corollary II we get $\gamma(A^*) = \frac{\gamma(B)}{p}$ and $\gamma(B^*) = \frac{\gamma(B)}{q}$ and this yields the assertion for t rational.

Lemma III. Let $B \subset \mathbb{N}$ be an infinite set, then for every $u \in (0, 1)$ there exists $B_1 \subset B$ that

$$\lim_{N\to\infty} \frac{B_1(N)}{B(N)} = u.$$

Proof: If $u = \frac{1}{v}$, then the set $B_1 = \{b_{[vn]}; n \in \mathbb{N}\}$ satisfies the Lemma III. $\qquad \square$

Let $t > 0$ be a real number. If $r > t$ is a rational number then $u = \frac{t}{r} < 1$. Let B_1 be the set from Lemma III. Then

$$\lim_{N\to\infty} \frac{A(N)}{B_1(N)} = r$$

thus $\gamma(A) = r\gamma(B_1) \leq r\gamma(B)$. Since $r > t$ is arbitrary, we obtain $\gamma(A) \leq t\gamma(B)$. The assumption is equivalent to

$$\lim_{N\to\infty} \frac{B(N)}{A(N)} = \frac{1}{t},$$

thus by the same procedure, we obtain $\gamma(B) \leq \frac{1}{t}\gamma(A)$. $\qquad \square$

Corollary V. Let γ be extension of asymptotic density. For every $A \subset \mathbb{N}$ and $m \in \mathbb{N}$ we have $\gamma(mA) = \frac{\gamma(A)}{m}$.

Buck's Measure Density

In 1946, R.C. Buck introduced measure density in his paper [BUC]. This notion is an analogy of Jordan measure on a closed interval.

Let us denote by $\mathcal{D}_0$ the system of all subsets of $\mathbb{N}$ which can be represented as the union of a finite number of arithmetic progressions. Clearly, $\mathcal{D}_0 \subset \mathcal{D}$. With respect to Buck's original notation, we shall denote the restriction of asymptotic density in the system $\mathcal{D}_0$ by Δ. Thus for every $H \in \mathcal{D}_0$ we have $\Delta(H) = d(H)$. We see immediately that $\mathcal{D}_0$ is an algebra of sets, and Δ is a finitely additive probability measure on $\mathcal{D}_0$. For $S \subset \mathbb{N}$ the value

$$\mu^*(S) = \inf\{\Delta(H); S \subset H \wedge H \in \mathcal{D}_0\}$$

is called the *Buck's measure density* or shortly only *measure density* of the set S [vi].

Every union of finite number arithmetic progression can be represented as disjoint union of arithmetic progressions with the same modul thus the definition of measure density has equivalent form

$$\mu^*(S) = \inf\left\{\frac{k}{m}; S \subset \bigcup_{j=1}^{k} r_j + (m), r_j, k, m \in \mathbb{N}\right\}.$$

Thus we see:

i) **If $S \subset \mathbb{N}$ then S has a nonempty intersection with each arithmetic progression if and only if $\mu^*(S) = 1$.** Thus, for example, $\mu^*(\{n + n!; n \in \mathbb{N}\}) = 1$, from the other side, we see that $d(\{n + n!; n \in \mathbb{N}\}) = 0$.

Directly from the definition we obtain:

ii) **For $H \in \mathcal{D}_0$ we have $\mu^*(H) = \Delta(H)$.**

Using the properties of arithmetic progression we prove the following inequalities:

For every $S_1, S_2 \subset \mathbb{N}$ there holds

iii) $S_1 \subset S_2 \Longrightarrow \mu^*(S_1) \leq \mu^*(S_2)$

iv) $\mu^*(S_1 \cup S_2) + \mu^*(S_1 \cap S_2) \leq \mu^*(S_1) + \mu^*(S_2)$.

The item iii) is trivial. We prove iv). Let $\varepsilon > 0$, then from the definition we have that there exists $H_1, H_2 \in \mathcal{D}_0$, that $S_1 \subset H_1, S_2 \subset H_2$ and

$$\mu^*(S_1) \leq \Delta(H_1) \leq \mu^*(S_1) + \varepsilon, \ \mu^*(S_2) \leq \Delta(H_2) \leq \mu^*(S_2) + \varepsilon,$$

since Δ is a finitely additive measure on $\mathcal{D}_0$ we have

$$\mu^*(S_1 \cup S_2) \leq \Delta(H_1 \cup H_2) = \Delta(H_1) + \Delta(H_2) - \Delta(H_1 \cap H_2),$$

this implies

$$\mu^*(S_1 \cup S_2) + \Delta(H_1 \cap H_2) \leq \Delta(H_1) + \Delta(H_2)$$

[vi]Let us remark that the original definition of Buck's measure density is slightly different. For two sets A, B we shall denote $A \simeq B$ if and only if $A \prec B$ and $B \prec A$, symbol $\prec$ is defined on page 24. Then in [BUC] $\mathcal{D}_0$ denotes the system of all sets H that $H \simeq a_1 + (m_1) \cup ... \cup a_k + (m_k)$, $\Delta(H) = d(H)$ and $\mu^*(S) = \inf\{\Delta(H); S \prec H, H \in \mathcal{D}_0\}$.

and so considering that $\mu^*(S_1 \cap S_2) \leq \Delta(H_1 \cap H_2)$, we get

$$\mu^*(S_1 \cup S_2) + \mu^*(S_1 \cap S_2) \leq \mu^*(S_1) + \mu^*(S_2) + 2\varepsilon.$$

For $\varepsilon \to 0^+$ we obtain the assertion.

From iii) it follows that $\mu^*(S) + \mu^*(\mathbb{N} \setminus S) \geq 1$ for every $S \subset \mathbb{N}$. A set S will be called *Buck's measurable* or shortly *measurable* if and only if

$$\mu^*(S) + \mu^*(\mathbb{N} \setminus S) = 1.$$

We denote the system of all measurable sets by $\mathcal{D}_\mu$.

v) **The system $\mathcal{D}_\mu$ is a set algebra and the restriction $\mu = \mu^*|_{\mathcal{D}_\mu}$ is a finitely probability measure on $\mathcal{D}_\mu$.**

Proof. It suffices to prove that $\mathcal{D}_\mu$ containing arbitrary two sets also contains their union. Let $A, B \in \mathcal{D}_\mu$, then from iii) we have

$$\mu^*(\mathbb{N} \setminus (A \cup B)) + \mu^*(\mathbb{N} \setminus (A \cap B)) \leq 2 - (\mu^*(A) + \mu^*(B)),$$

and by addition the inequality iii) we obtain

$$\mu^*(\mathbb{N} \setminus (A \cup B)) + \mu^*(\mathbb{N} \setminus (A \cap B)) + \mu^*(A \cup B) + \mu^*(A \cap B) \leq 2,$$

thus

$$\mu^*(\mathbb{N} \setminus (A \cup B)) + \mu^*(A \cup B) = 1. \quad \square$$

From the definition of measure density we get:

vi) **A set $S \subset \mathbb{N}$ is measurable if and only if for arbitrary $\varepsilon > 0$ there exist the sets $H_1, H_2 \in \mathcal{D}_0$ such that $H_1 \subset S \subset H_2$ and $\Delta(H_2) - \Delta(H_1) < \varepsilon$.** This yields:

vii) **Each measurable set has asymptotic density which coincides with its measure density.**

viii) **Let $A \in \mathcal{D}_\mu$ and $\mu(A) = 1$. Let $B_1 \in \mathcal{D}_\mu$ and $B_2 \subseteq \mathbb{N}$. If $B_1 \cap A = B_2 \cap A$, then $B_2 \in \mathcal{D}_\mu$ and $\mu(B_2) = \mu(B_1)$.**

Using v) and vi) we can transfer the Niven's result, Theorem 3, page 20 for the case of Buck's measurability in a stronger form. Let us recall that for $S \subset \mathbb{N}$ and p prime S_p is the set of all elements of S divisible by p but not by p^2.

Theorem 1. Let $\{p_n\}$ be such sequence of different primes that

$$\sum_{n=1}^{\infty} \frac{1}{p_n} = \infty. \tag{$*$}$$

Then for arbitrary set $S \subset \mathbb{N}$ it holds

$$S \in \mathcal{D}_\mu \iff \forall n = 1, 2, \ldots; S_{p_n} \in \mathcal{D}_\mu.$$

And in this case

$$\mu(S) = \lim_{N \to \infty} \mu\left(\bigcup_{n=1}^{N} S_{p_n}\right).$$

Proof. The assertion follows immediately from the fact that the set M_N, defined on page 20, belongs to $\mathcal{D}_0$ and from the inclusion $(**)$ also on page 20. $\qquad\square$

Corollary 1. For an arbitrary set $S \subset \mathbb{N}$ it holds

$$\mu^*(S) = 0 \Longleftrightarrow \forall n = 1, 2, ...; \mu^*(S_{p_n}) = 0.$$

As an immediate consequence we get that every set of powers $\mathbb{N}^k = \{n^k, k \in \mathbb{N}\}$ for $k = 2, 3, ...$ is measurable and $\mu(\mathbb{N}^k) = 0$. Similarly, the set of primes is measurable and its measure density is 0.

Corollary 2. Let $B \in \mathcal{D}_\mu$ and $\mu(B) = 1$. Let $\{p_i\}$ be such a sequence of primes that $\sum_{i=1}^{\infty} p_i^{-1} = \infty$. **Put $A = \bigcup_{i=1}^{\infty} p_i B$. Then $A \in \mathcal{D}_\mu$ and $\mu(A) = 1$.**

Proof. Consider $(\mathbb{N} \setminus A)_{p_i}$. Let $n \in (\mathbb{N} \setminus A)_{p_i}$. Then $n \notin A$ and $n = p_i \cdot m$, $(m, p_i) = 1$. If $m \in B$, then $n \in p_i B$ and so $n \in A$—a contradiction. Thus $m \in \mathbb{N} \setminus B$, this yields $(\mathbb{N} \setminus A)_{p_i} \subset p_i(\mathbb{N} \setminus B)$, therefore $\mu((\mathbb{N} \setminus A)_{p_i}) = 0$. From Theorem 1, we now have that $\mu(\mathbb{N} \setminus A) = 0$, and the assertion follows.

The product of the arithmetic progressions

In the paper [ST], the asymptotic density of the product $(a_1 + (m_1))(a_2 + (m_2))$, $(a_1, m_1) = 1$, $(a_2, m_2) = 1$, was studied, where for two $A_1, A_2 \subseteq \mathbb{N}$ we put $A_1 \cdot A_2 = \{n_1 \cdot n_2; n_1 \in A_1 \wedge n_2 \in A_2\}$. Using the Theorem 1, we transfer now the ideas from this paper for the Buck's measurability.

We start by following assertion

Lemma 1. Let $\{p_i^{(1)}\}, \ldots, \{p_i^{(k)}\}$ are such sequences of primes $\sum_{i=1}^{\infty} \frac{1}{p_i^{(l)}} = \infty$, **for $l = 1, \ldots, k$. Put $A \subseteq \mathbb{N}$ in the following way:**

$$n \in A \iff n = p_{i_1}^{(1)} \cdots p_{i_k}^{(k)} m, \quad m \in \mathbb{N}.$$

Then $A \in \mathcal{D}_\mu$, and $\mu(A) = 1$.

Proof. By induction. If $k = 1$, then

$$A = \bigcup_{i=1}^{\infty} (p_i^{(1)}),,$$

and the assertion follows from Corollary 2.

Let the statement hold for $k - 1$. Now, A can be represented as

$$A = \bigcup_{i=1}^{\infty} p_i^{(k)} B, \tag{1}$$

where $n \in B \Leftrightarrow n = p_{i_1}^{(1)} \cdots p_{i_{k-1}}^{(k-1)} \cdot m$, and from the induction assumption we have $B \in \mathcal{D}_\mu$ and $\mu(B) = 1$, and so Corollary 2 and (1) imply the assertion.

Theorem I. $m \in \mathbb{N}$, $m \geq 1$ and $a_1, \ldots, a_k \in \mathbb{N}$ and $(a_i, m) = 1$, $i = 1, \ldots, k - 1$. **Put**

$$S = (a_1 + (m)) \cdots (a_{k-1} + (m))(a_k + (m)).$$

Then $S \in \mathcal{D}_\mu$ **and** $\mu(S) = \frac{1}{m}$.

Proof. Clearly ,

$$S \subset a_1 a_2 \cdots a_k + (m). \tag{2}$$

Let $\{p_i^{(j)}\}$ be the sequence of all primes from $a_j + (m)$, $j = 1, \ldots, k - 1$. From the Dirichlet theorem (cf. [S-B], [NAR]) we have $\sum_{i=1}^{\infty} \frac{1}{p_i^{(j)}} = \infty$, $j = 1, \ldots, k - 1$.

Let us define the set A as in Lemma 1. Assume that

$$b \in (a_1 \cdots a_k + (m)) \cap A$$

then

$$b \equiv a_1 \cdots a_k \pmod{m}$$

and

$$b = p_{i_1}^{(1)} \cdots p_{i_{k-1}}^{(k-1)} \cdot b'$$

thus

$$p_{i_1}^{(1)} \cdots p_{i_{k-1}}^{(k-1)} \cdot b' \equiv a_1 \cdots a_k \pmod{m}. \tag{3}$$

For every $j = 1, \ldots, k - 1$ we have $p_{i_j} \equiv a_j \pmod{m}$ and so (3) yields

$$a_1 \cdots a_{k-1} b' \equiv a_1 \cdots a_k \pmod{m}.$$

For $j = 1, \ldots, k - 1$ we have $(a_j, m) = 1$, and thus from the last congruence it follows $b' \equiv a_k$ $\pmod{m}$, and so $b \in S$. We have proven

$$(a_1 \cdots a_k + (m)) \cap A \subseteq S \cap A.$$

From (2) we obtain the other inclusion, thus

$$S \cap A = (a_1 \cdots a_k + (m)) \cap A,$$

and the assertion follows from viii).

Theorem II. Let $m_1, \ldots, m_k$ **be positive integers with the same primes in the canonic representation. Let** $a_1, \ldots, a_k$ **be such positive integers that** $(a_j, m_j) = 1$, $j = 1, \ldots, k$. **Then the set**

$$S = (a_1 + (m_1)) \cdots (a_k + (m_k))$$

is measurable.

Proof. Put $m = [m_1, \ldots, m_k]$. Then $(a_j, m) = 1$, $j = 1, \ldots, k$, and every $a_j + (m_j)$ can be represented in the form

$$a_j + (m_j) = \bigcup_{k=0}^{\frac{m}{m_j} - 1} b_{j,k} + (m),$$

where $b_{j,k} = a_j + k \cdot m_j$. Clearly, $(b_{j,k}, m) = 1$. Thus, the set S is a finite union of sets of the type as in Theorem 1, therefore i) yields $S \in \mathcal{D}_\mu$.

Unfortunately, we are not able to guarantee that the "summands" from the last proof are disjoint, and so we cannot determine the value $\mu(S)$.

Darboux property

We prove that measure density has the Darboux on the algebra of the measurable sets. We start
with the equivalent form of the property iv):
viii) **A set** $S \subset \mathbb{N}$ **is measurable in and only if for arbitrary** $\varepsilon > 0$ **there exist the sets**
$S_1, S_2 \in \mathcal{D}_\mu$ **such that** $S_1 \subset S \subset S_2$ **and** $\mu(S_2) - \mu(S_1) < \varepsilon.$

Using this property, we prove a certain form of σ - additivity:
Theorem 2. Let $A_n \in \mathcal{D}_\mu, n = 1, 2, \dots$ **If**

$$\lim_{N \to \infty} \mu^* \left(\bigcup_{n=N}^{\infty} A_n \right) = 0, \qquad (*)$$

then $\bigcup_{n=1}^{\infty} A_n \in \mathcal{D}_\mu.$ **If, moreover,** $A_n \cap A_m = \emptyset$ **for** $m \neq n$ **then**

$$\mu\left(\bigcup_{n=1}^{\infty} A_n\right) = \sum_{n=1}^{\infty} \mu(A_n).$$

Proof. From the assumption $(*)$, it follows that for $\varepsilon >$ there exist N and $H \in \mathcal{D}_0$ that

$$\bigcup_{n=N}^{\infty} A_n \subset H, \ \Delta(H) < \varepsilon,$$

thus

$$\bigcup_{n=1}^{N-1} A_n \subset \bigcup_{n=1}^{\infty} A_n \subset \bigcup_{n=1}^{N-1} A_n \cup H,$$

and the assertion follows.   □

Theorem 3. Let $A, B \in \mathcal{D}_\mu, B \subset A$ **and** $\mu(B) < \mu(A)$. **Then for every** $\alpha \in (\mu(B), \mu(A))$
there exists a set $C \in \mathcal{D}_\mu$ **that** $B \subset C \subset A$ **and** $\mu(C) = \alpha$.
Proof. Suppose that $B = \emptyset$. From the assumption of measurability of A we obtain that there
exists $m \in \mathbb{N}, m > 1$ and $r_1, \dots, r_s$ non negative integers incongruent modulo m that

$$r_1 + (m) \cup \dots \cup r_s + (m) \subset A$$

and

$$\alpha < \frac{s}{m} \leq \mu(A).$$

Let

$$\alpha = \sum_{k=1}^{\infty} \frac{c_k}{m^k}, \ 0 \leq c_k \leq m - 1, k = 1, 2, \dots$$

be the $m-$ adic expansion of α. Put $C_1 = \cup_{i=1}^{c_1} r_i + (m)$. Clearly $c_1 < s$ thus $C_1 \cap r_s + (m) = \emptyset$.
Let us define the sets $C_k, k \geq 2$ as follows. If $c_k = 0$ then $C_k = \emptyset$. Otherwise

$$C_k = \bigcup_{j=1}^{c_k} r_s + jm^{k-1} + (m^k).$$

The sets $C_k, k = 1, 2, \ldots$ belong to $\mathcal{D}_\mu$ and $\mu(C_k) = \frac{c_k}{m^k}$. Suppose that $C_k \cap C_l \neq \emptyset$ for some $k < l$. Then for suitable $a, b \in \mathbb{N}$ it holds

$$j_1 m^{k-1} + a m^k = j_2 m^{l-1} + b m^l, \ 1 \le j_1 \le m - 1, \ 1 \le j_2 \le m - 1,$$

therefore $m^k | j_1 m^{k-1}$ - contradiction. We proved that the sets $C_k, k = 1, 2, \ldots$ are disjoint. Moreover $C_l \subset r_s + (m^k)$ for $l > k$. This yields $\cup_{l=k+1}^\infty C_l \subset r_s + (m^k)$ and so $\mu^*(\cup_{l=k+1}^\infty C_l) \le \frac{1}{m^k}$. Therefore from Theorem 2, we get that the set $C = \cup_{k=1}^\infty C_k \subset A$ is measurable and $\mu(C) = \alpha$.

If $B \neq \emptyset$, then we can make the same considerations for the set $A \setminus B$ and the number $\alpha - \mu(B)$.   □

Theorem 4. **Let $\{m_k\}$ be a sequence of positive integers such that $(m_i, m_j) = 1$ for $i \neq j$. Then**

a) **for $N = 1, 2, \ldots$ it holds $\bigcup\limits_{k=1}^{N} (m_k) \in \mathcal{D}_\mu$ and**

$$\mu\left(\bigcup_{k=1}^{N} (m_k) \right) = 1 - \prod_{k=1}^{N} \left(1 - \frac{1}{m_k} \right).$$

b)

$$\mu^*\left(\bigcup_{k=1}^{\infty} (m_k) \right) = 1$$

c)

$$\mu^*\left(\mathbb{N} \setminus \bigcup_{k=1}^{\infty} (m_k) \right) = \prod_{k=1}^{\infty} \left(1 - \frac{1}{m_k} \right).$$

Proof. Part a) is trivial. Part b) is based on the Chinese reminder theorem, because the system of congruences $x \equiv -1 \pmod{m_1}, \ldots, x \equiv -n \pmod{m_n}$ is solvable, thus the set $\bigcup\limits_{k=1}^{\infty} (m_k)$ contains arbitrary, long sequence of consecutive integers. For $N = 1, 2, \ldots$ it holds

$$\mathbb{N} \setminus \bigcup_{k=1}^{\infty} (m_k) \subset \mathbb{N} \setminus \bigcup_{k=1}^{N} (m_k),$$

and so from a) it follows

$$\mu^*\left(\mathbb{N} \setminus \bigcup_{k=1}^{\infty} (m_k) \right) \le \prod_{k=1}^{\infty} \left(1 - \frac{1}{m_k} \right).$$

Theorem 1, page 12, yields the opposite inequality, thus c) is proved.   □

The function α_p

In the paper [Sal1], Tibor Šalát investigated the arithmetic function α_p given for the prime number p and $n \in \mathbb{N}$ as the exponent of the maximal power of p, which divides n thus

$$\alpha_p(n) = \max\{k = 0, 1, 2, ...; p^k | n\}.$$

It is proven that for every prime number p the set

$$M^p = \{n \in \mathbb{N}; \alpha_p(n) | n\}$$

has the asymptotic density and

$$d(M^p) = \sum_{k=1}^{\infty} \frac{p-1}{kp^{k-\alpha_p(k)+1}}.$$

Using Theorem 2, this result was improved in the paper [PAS2] as follows:

Proposition. For every p- prime the set M^p is measurable and

$$\mu(M^p) = \frac{p-1}{p^2} \sum_{j=0}^{\infty} \ln \frac{p^{p^{j+1}} - 1}{(p^{p^j} - 1)^p}.$$

For proof, we shall use the following

Lemma. For every p- prime there holds

$$\sum_{k=1}^{\infty} \frac{p-1}{kp^{k-\alpha_p(k)+1}} = \frac{p-1}{p^2} \sum_{j=0}^{\infty} \ln \frac{p^{p^{j+1}} - 1}{(p^{p^j} - 1)^p}.$$

Proof. We shall say for the prime number p and $x \in < 0, 1)$ there holds

$$\sum_{(p,q)=1} \frac{x^q}{q} = \frac{1}{p} \ln \frac{1 - x^p}{(1-x)^p}. \qquad (*)$$

This equality follows directly from

$$\sum_{(p,q)=1} \frac{x^q}{q} = \sum_{n=1}^{\infty} \frac{x^n}{n} - \sum_{m=1}^{\infty} \frac{x^{pm}}{pm}$$

and

$$-\ln(1-x) = \sum_{n=1}^{\infty} \frac{x^n}{n}.$$

Now we get

$$\sum_{k=1}^{\infty} \frac{p-1}{kp^{k-\alpha_p(k)+1}} = \frac{p-1}{p} \sum_{j=0}^{\infty} \sum_{\alpha_p(k)=j} \frac{1}{kp^{k-j}}.$$

If $\alpha_p(k) = j$ then $k = p^j q, (p, q) = 1$. Therefore

$$\sum_{\alpha_p(k)=j} \frac{1}{kp^{k-j}} = \sum_{(p,q)=1} \frac{1}{p^j qp^{p^j q - j}} = \sum_{(p,q)=1} \frac{1}{qp^{p^j q}}$$

and the assertion we obtain from $(*)$.   □

Proof of Proposition. Clearly ,

$$M^p = \bigcup_{k=1}^{\infty} B_k \qquad (*)$$

where

$$B_k = \{n \in \mathbb{N}; \alpha_p(n) = k \wedge k | n\}.$$

A positive integer n belongs to B_k, $k = 1, 2, \dots$ if and only it is of the form $n = kp^{k-\alpha_p(k)}m$ where $(m, p) = 1$. Thus we have

$$B_k = (kp^{k-\alpha_p(k)}) \setminus (kp^{k-\alpha_p(k)+1}).$$

This yields $B_k \in \mathcal{D}_\mu$ and $\mu(B_k) = \frac{p-1}{kp^{k-\alpha_p(k)+1}}$, for $k = 1, 2, \dots$. For $k > K$ there holds $B_k \subset (p^K)$ thus $\mu^*(\cup_{k>K} B_k) \le \frac{1}{p^K}$ and Theorem 2 yields $M_p \in \mathcal{D}_\mu$. Moreover the sets $B_k, k = 1, 2, \dots$ are mutually disjoint and so from Theorem 2 we obtain

$$\mu(M^p) = \sum_{k=1}^{\infty} \frac{p-1}{kp^{k-\alpha_p(k)+1}},$$

and from Lemma, we obtain the assertion.   □

$\mathcal{I}_\mu$ - convergence

Let us denote by $\mathcal{I}_\mu$ the system of all subsets of $\mathbb{N}$ having the measure density of 0. Then I_μ is an admissible ideal. We construct an example which shows that in this case, the $\mathcal{I}_\mu$ - convergence is not equivalent with $\mathcal{I}_\mu^*$ - convergence.

Put for $k \in \mathbb{N} \cup \{0\}$

$$B_k = \{k + n!; n \in \mathbb{N}\}.$$

Clearly, $B_k \prec k + (m)$ for $m \in \mathbb{N}$, thus $\mu(B_k) = 0$, $k = 0, 1, 2, \dots$. Let us define the sequence $\{f_n\}$ as follows. If $n \in \cup_{k=1}^{\infty} B_k$, then $f_n = \frac{1}{l+1}$, where $l = \min\{k; n \in B_k\}$, $f_n = 0$ otherwise. For $\varepsilon > 0$ we have $\{n; f_n \ge \varepsilon\} \subset \cup_{k \le \frac{1}{\varepsilon}} B_k$ thus $\mu(\{n; f_n \ge \varepsilon\}) = 0$ and so $\mathcal{I}_\mu - \lim f_n = 0$.

Suppose that $A \in \mathcal{D}_\mu$ and $\mu(A) \ge 0$. Then for suitable $m, \in \mathbb{N}, k = 0, 1, \dots$ there holds $k + (m) \prec A$ thus $B_k \prec A$. Therefore $f_n \ge \frac{1}{k+1}$ for infinitely many $n \in A$ and so does not hold $\lim_A f_n = 0$. Therefore, in this case, it does not hold that $\mathcal{I}_\mu^* - \lim f_n = 0$.

Limit formula

Let us denote for $S \subset \mathbb{N}, B \in \mathbb{N}$ by $R(S : B)$, the maximum number of elements of S incongruent modulo B. A sequence of positive integers $\{B_n\}$ is called *complete* if and only if for each $m \in \mathbb{N}$ exists $n_0 \in \mathbb{N}$ that $m | B_n, n \ge n_0$.

An important rule in our next considerations will have following formula:

Theorem 5. Let $\{B_n\}$ be a complete sequence. Then for every $S \subset \mathbb{N}$ we have

$$\mu^*(S) = \lim_{n \to \infty} \frac{R(S : B_n)}{B_n}.$$

Proof. Let $k_n = R(S : B_n), n = 1, 2, ..$ then

$$S \subset \bigcup_{j=1}^{k_n} r_j^{(n)} + (B_n),$$

where $r_1^{(n)}, ..., r_{k_n}^{(n)}$ are incongruent elements of S. Thus $\mu^*(S) \leq \frac{R(S:B_n)}{B_n}$.

Let $\varepsilon > 0$, then there exists $m \in \mathbb{N}$ and $b_1, ..., b_s \in \mathbb{N}$ that

$$S \subset \bigcup_{j=1}^{s} b_j + (m), \qquad\qquad (*)$$

and

$$\frac{s}{m} \leq \mu^*(s) + \varepsilon. \qquad\qquad (**)$$

For a suitable n_0, we have that $m | B_n, n \geq n_0$, therefore the union from $(*)$ can be represented in the form

$$\bigcup_{j=1}^{s} b_j + (m) = \bigcup_{j=1}^{s_n} t_j^{(n)} + (B_n),$$

where $\frac{s_n}{B_n} = \frac{s}{m}$. From the inclusion $(*)$ we get that $R(S : B_n) \leq s_n$ for $n \geq n_0$ and by $(**)$ this yields $\frac{R(S:B_n)}{B_n} \leq \mu^*(S) + \varepsilon$ for $n \geq n_0$. $\qquad\qquad\square$

Let $C \subset \mathbb{N}, m \in \mathbb{N}$, let us denote $C + (m) = \cup_{c \in C} c + (m)$. Clearly, $C + (m) \in \mathcal{D}_0$ and $\Delta(C + (m)) = \frac{R(C:m)}{m}$. Let $\{B_n\}$ be a complete sequence. There holds for all n

$$A + (B_n) \cup ((\mathbb{N} \setminus A) + (B_n)) = \mathbb{N}$$

thus

$$\Delta(A + (B_n) \cup ((\mathbb{N} \setminus A) + (B_n))) = 1$$

this implies

$$\frac{R(A : B_n)}{B_n} + \frac{R((\mathbb{N} \setminus A) : B_n)}{B_n} - \Delta(A + (B_n) \cap ((\mathbb{N} \setminus A) + (B_n))) = 1.$$

From this equality, we see that A is measurable if and only if

$$\lim_{n \to \infty} \Delta(A + (B_n) \cap ((\mathbb{N} \setminus A) + (B_n))) = 0.$$

Proposition. For $S \subset \mathbb{N}$ and $a, m \in \mathbb{N}$ we have

$$\mu^*(S + a) = \mu^*(S), \ \mu^*(mS) = \frac{\mu^*(S)}{m}.$$

Proof. The first equality is obvious and the second one follows from the fact that $R(mS : mB_n) = R(S : B_n)$ for an arbitrary complete sequence $\{B_n\}$, and the sequence $\{mB_n\}$ is also complete. $\qquad\square$

Theorem 6. Let $\{B_n\}$ be a complete sequence. The a set $A \subset \mathbb{N}$ is measurable if and only if for the arbitrary sequence $\{k_1^{(n)}...k_{B_n}^{(n)}\}, n = 1, 2, ...$ of complete reminder systems modulo $B_n, n = 1, 2, ...$ it holds

$$\lim_{n \to \infty} \frac{1}{B_n} \sum_{j=1}^{B_n} \chi_A(k_j^{(n)}) = c, \qquad (*)$$

and in this case $c = \mu^*(A)$.

Proof. Let A be measurable. Clearly

$$\sum_{j=1}^{B_n} \chi_A(k_j^{(n)}) \le R(A : B_n)$$

$$\sum_{j=1}^{B_n} \chi_{\mathbb{N} \setminus A}(k_j^{(n)}) \le R(\mathbb{N} \setminus A : B_n).$$

Thus

$$\limsup_{n \to \infty} \frac{1}{B_n} \sum_{j=1}^{B_n} \chi_A(k_j^{(n)}) \le \mu^*(A).$$

From the equality $1 = \chi_A + \chi_{\mathbb{N} \setminus A}$ we get

$$1 = \frac{1}{B_n} \sum_{j=1}^{B_n} \chi_A(k_j^{(n)}) + \frac{1}{B_n} \sum_{j=1}^{B_n} \chi_{\mathbb{N} \setminus A}(k_j^{(n)}) \le$$

$$\le \frac{1}{B_n} \sum_{j=1}^{B_n} \chi_A(k_j^{(n)}) + \frac{R(\mathbb{N} \setminus A : B_n)}{B_n}. \qquad (**)$$

If

$$\limsup_{n \to \infty} \frac{1}{B_n} \sum_{j=1}^{B_n} \chi_A(k_j^{(n)}) \le \mu^*(A).$$

then for suitable $\alpha < \mu^*(A)$ and subsequent $\{n_i\}$, we have

$$\lim_{i \to \infty} \frac{1}{B_{n_i}} \sum_{j=1}^{B_{n_i}} \chi_A(k_j^{(n_i)}) = \alpha,$$

and from $(**)$ we obtain

$$1 \leq \alpha + \mu^*(\mathbb{N} \setminus A) = \alpha + 1 - \mu^*(A) < 1,$$

which is a contradiction.

Let $(*)$ hold. Consider $\{k_1^{(n)}, ..., k_{q(n)}^{(n)}\}$ the maximal set of elements of A incongruent modulo B_n, $n = 1, 2, ...$, where $q(n) = R(A : B_n)$. This set, we can complete with suitable positive integers $\{k_{q(n)+1}^{(n)}, ..., k_{B_n}^{(n)}\}$ to complete the reminder system modulo B_n. Clearly

$$\frac{1}{B_n} \sum_{j=1}^{B_n} \chi_A(k_j^{(n)}) = \frac{q(n)}{B_n} = \frac{R(A : B_n)}{B_n},$$

thus For $n \to \infty$ we obtain from $(*)$ that $c = \mu^*(A)$.

Analogously, let $\{l_1^{(n)}, ..., l_{r(n)}^{(n)}\}$ be the the maximal set of elements of $\mathbb{N} \setminus A$ incongruent modulo B_n, $n = 1, 2, ...$ This set, we can complete with suitable positive integers $\{l_{r(n)+1}^{(n)}, ..., l_{B_n}^{(n)}\}$ to complete the reminder system modulo B_n, we get

$$\frac{1}{B_n} \sum_{j=1}^{B_n} \chi_{\mathbb{N} \setminus A}(l_j^{(n)}) = \frac{r(n)}{B_n} = \frac{R(\mathbb{N} \setminus A : B_n)}{B_n}.$$

This yields for $n \to \infty$ considering that $1 = \chi_A + \chi_{\mathbb{N} \setminus A}$ that $\mu^*(\mathbb{N} \setminus A) = 1 - \mu^*(A)$. □

Uniform distribution in $\mathbb{Z}$

Using the analogy between the intervals and the arithmetic progressions, I. Niven defined uniform distribution of the sequences of integers.

Let $\{x_n\}$ be a sequence of positive integers and $S \subset \mathbb{N}$. Put $A(\{x_n\}, S) = \{n \in \mathbb{N}; x_n \in S\}$. If m is a positive integer, then this sequence is called *uniformly distributed modulo* m if and only if for an arbitrary integer r there holds $A(\{x_n\}, r + (m)) \in \mathcal{D}$ and $d(A(\{x_n\}, r + (m))) = \frac{1}{m}$. A sequence of positive integers is called *uniformly distributed in* $\mathbb{Z}$ if it is uniformly distributed modulo m for every $m \in \mathbb{N}$ [vii].

An example of a sequence uniformly distributed in $\mathbb{Z}$ is the sequence $\{n\}$ of all positive integers in the natural order, or the sequence $\{n+n!\}$. The asymptotic density set of the elements of second one is 0.

Some sequences uniformly distributed in $\mathbb{Z}$ we can obtain from the following result from [D-M]:

[vii]The name uniformly distributed in $\mathbb{Z}$ is taken from the monograph [K-N], and it can be considered also for the sequences of integers, for this reason we say in $\mathbb{Z}$.

Proposition A. Let $S \in \mathcal{D}$ and $d(S) = 1$. Let us denote $S = \{s_1 < s_2 < ...\}$. Then the sequence $\{s_n\}$ is uniformly distributed in $\mathbb{Z}$.
   Proof: The condition $d(S) = 1$ yields

$$d(S \cap r + (m)) = \frac{1}{m} \qquad (i)$$

for every arithmetic progression $r + (m)$.
   For each $N \in \mathbb{N}$ there exists a suitable $k_N \in \mathbb{N}$ such that $s_{k_N} \leq N < s_{k_N+1}$. From the condition $d(S) = 1$, we get

$$\lim_{N \to \infty} \frac{k_N}{N} = 1. \qquad (ii)$$

We see that for every $N \in \mathbb{N}$ there holds $A(\{s_n\}, r + (m))(N) = (S \cap r + (m))(k_N)$. Thus

$$\frac{A(\{s_n\}, r + (m))(N)}{N} = \frac{(S \cap r + (m))(k_N)}{k_N} \frac{k_N}{N},$$

and the assertion follows from (i) and (ii).   □
   If we consider the sequence $\{n + n!, 2n + n!\}$ then the measure density of the sets of its element is 1, but it is easy to see that it is not uniformly distributed in $\mathbb{Z}$. In this case the following holds:
   Proposition B. Let $S \subset \mathbb{N}$ then $\mu^*(S) = 1$ if and only if S can be arranged to a sequence uniformly distributed in $\mathbb{Z}$.
   Proof. The sequence uniformly distributed in $\mathbb{Z}$ contains elements, which belong to a arbitrary arithmetic progression, thus from i) of this chapter we obtain that the set of all its elements has the measure density of 1.
   Suppose that for $S \subset \mathbb{N}$ there holds $\mu^*(S) = 1$. From i) in this chapter, we obtain that there exists a one to one sequence $\{x_n\}$ of S that

$$x_n \equiv n \pmod{n!}.$$

Thus $\{x_n\}$ is uniformly distributed in $\mathbb{Z}$. If the set $S \setminus \{x_n, n = 1, 2, ...\}$ is finite then the proof is finished. If not, then denote $S \setminus \{x_n, n = 1, 2, ...\} = \{x'_n, n = 1, 2, ...\}$. Let us define the sequence $\{y_n\}$ as follows

$$y_n = x_n, \; n \neq k^2$$
$$y_n = x_{k^2}, \; n = (2k)^2$$
$$y_n = x'_k, \; n = (2k+1)^2.$$

The sequence $\{y_n\}$ is a one to one sequence of all elements of S and it can be easily proved that it is uniformly distributed in $\mathbb{Z}$.   □

   Let us recall now the mean value of the arithmetic function, from page 39. If f is an arithmetic function with a period $m \in \mathbb{N}$ then

$$E(f) = \lim_{N \to \infty} E_N(F) = \frac{1}{m} \sum_{j=1}^{m} f(j).$$

Every periodic arithmetic function can be expressed as a linear combination of indicator functions of arithmetic progressions thus we have following analogy of Weyl's criterion :

Proposition C. A sequence of positive integers $\{x_n\}$ is uniformly distributed in $\mathbb{Z}$ if and only if

$$\lim_{N \to \infty} \frac{1}{N} \sum_{n=1}^{N} f(x_n) = E(f)$$

for every periodic arithmetic function, f.

Every arithmetic function, f periodic modulo $m \in \mathbb{N}$ can be expressed in the form $f(n) = \sum_{h=0}^{m} c_h \exp\left(2\pi i \frac{h}{m} n\right), n \in \mathbb{N}$, for suitable complex numbers $c_h, h = 0, ..., m-1$. Thus we get

Proposition D. A sequence of positive integers $\{x_n\}$ is uniformly distributed in $\mathbb{Z}$ if and only if

$$\lim_{N \to \infty} \frac{1}{N} \sum_{n=1}^{N} \exp\left(2\pi i \frac{h}{m} x_n\right) = 0$$

for every $h = 1, ..., m-1$.

Thus, for instance, the sequence of integer parts $\{[n\alpha]\}$ for α irrational, is uniformly distributed in $\mathbb{Z}$.

Now we recall the definition of polyadicly continuous arithmetic function from page 31. Every periodic arithmetic function is polyadicly continuous, and every polyadicly continuous arithmetic function can be uniformly approximated by a periodic function. Thus we can extend the previous criterion to:

Proposition E. A sequence of positive integers $\{x_n\}$ is uniformly distributed in $\mathbb{Z}$ if and only if

$$\lim_{N \to \infty} \frac{1}{N} \sum_{n=1}^{N} f(x_n) = E(f)$$

for every polyadicly continuous arithmetic function, f.

Now we characterize the measurability by the uniform distribution in $\mathbb{Z}$.

Lemma. Let $S \subset \mathbb{N}$. Then there exists a sequence of positive integers $\{x_n\}, \{y_n\}$ uniformly distributed in $\mathbb{Z}$ and a sequence of positive integers $\{D_n\}$ such that

$$\lim_{k \to \infty} \frac{A(\{x_n\}, S)(D_k)}{D_k} = \mu^*(S) \tag{$*$}$$

and

$$\lim_{k \to \infty} \frac{A(\{y_n\}, S)(D_k)}{D_k} = 1 - \mu^*(\mathbb{N} \setminus S). \tag{$**$}$$

Proof. Let $\{B_n\}$ be an arbitrary complete sequence. Let us consider the system of complete reminder systems Z_s modulo B_s, such that Z_s contains exactly $R(S : B_s)$ incongruent elements modulo B_s from S and the rest $B_s - R(S : B_s)$ incongruent elements, we take from $\mathbb{N} \setminus S$. Put $D_s = \sum_{s=1}^{k} B_s$. We construct a sequence $\{x_n\}$ as follows: the first D_1 elements will be the elements of Z_1 arranged in such a way that $x_j \equiv j \pmod{B_1}, j = 1, ..., D_1$. Then the elements of Z_2 arranged in such a way that $x_j \equiv j \pmod{B_2}, j = D_1 + 1, ..., D_2$, if we have the D_k elements, then the next B_{k+1} will be the elements of Z_{k+1} arranged in such a way that $x_j \equiv j$ $\pmod{B_{k+1}}, j = D_k + 1, ..., D_{k+1}$. If $m \in \mathbb{N}$, then a for suitable k_0 we have $m | B_k, k \geq k_0$, thus $x_j \equiv j \pmod{m}$ for $j > D_{k_0}$ and so the sequence $\{x_n\}$ is uniformly distributed modulo m, therefore it is uniformly distributed in $\mathbb{Z}$. Clearly, there holds

$$A(\{x_n\}, S)(D_k) = \sum_{s=1}^{k} R(S : B_s).$$

From the previous, we have

$$\lim_{s \to \infty} \frac{R(\mathbb{N} \setminus S : B_s)}{B_s} = \mu^*(S),$$

and so from the Stolz theorem, we obtain that

$$\lim_{k \to \infty} \frac{A(\{x_n\}, S)(D_k)}{D_k} = \mu^*(S).$$

If we consider the system of complete reminder systems Z'_s modulo B_s, such that Z'_s contains exactly $R(\mathbb{N} \setminus S : B_s)$ incongruent elements modulo B_s from $\mathbb{N} \setminus S$ and the rest $B_s - R(\mathbb{N} \setminus S : B_s)$ incongruent elements we take from S, then by the same procedure as in the previous case we obtain the sequence $\{y_n\}$ uniformly distributed in $\mathbb{Z}$ satisfying $(**)$. $\qquad \square$

Theorem 7. Let $S \subset \mathbb{N}$. Then S is measurable if and only if the following two conditions hold:

a) **For every sequence $\{x_n\}$ uniformly distributed in $\mathbb{Z}$, it holds $A(\{x_n\}, S) \in \mathcal{D}$.**

b) **For every two sequences $\{x_n\}, \{y_n\}$ uniformly distributed in $\mathbb{Z}$ it holds $d(A(\{x_n\}, S))$**
   $= d(A(\{y_n\}, S))$.
   And, in this case, we have $d(A(\{x_n\}, S)) = \mu(S)$ for every sequence $\{x_n\}$ uniformly distributed in $\mathbb{Z}$.

Proof. From vi), page 39, we see immediately that every measurable set S satisfies a), b).

If the set S satisfies a), b) then from lemma we have that $\mu^*(S) = 1 - \mu^*(\mathbb{N} \setminus S)$ and the assertion follows. $\qquad \square$

Uniform Distribution With Respect To Measure Density

The notion of Buck's measure density gives us the possibility to transfer the Weyl's notion of uniform distribution uniform distribution of sequences from page 32 for this case.

The sequence $\{y_n\}, y_n \in\, <0, 1)$ is called *Buck's uniformly distributed* if and only if for every subinterval $I \subseteq\, <0, 1)$ the set $A(\{y_n\}, I)$ belongs to D_μ and

$$\mu(A(\{y_n\}, I)) = |I| \tag{4}$$

where $|I|$ is the length of I. Instead of Buck's uniformly distributed we shall write only *B.u.d.*
Remark that (iii) yields that every B.u.d. sequence is uniformly distributed in the sense (2).

Some elementary statements

Proposition 1. Let $\{y_n\}$ be a sequence of numbers from $<0, 1)$. Then $\{y_n\}$ is B.u.d if and only if

a) $\forall x \in (0, 1); \; A(<0, x)) \in D_\mu \wedge \mu(A(<0, x))) = x$.

b) $\forall x \in (0, 1); \; A(<0, x\,>) \in D_\mu \wedge \mu(A(<0, x\,>)) = x$.

Proof. Suppose that a) holds. For $x \in\, <0, 1)$ and $\varepsilon > 0$ we have $A(<0, x)) \subset A(<0, x\,>) \subset A(<0, x + \varepsilon))$. Thus (ii) yields $A(<0, x\,>) \in D_\mu$ and $x \le \mu(A <0, x\,>) \le x + \varepsilon$ and so for $\varepsilon \to 0^+$ we have $\mu(A <0, x\,>) = x$. Now for an arbitrary interval I (suppose for instance that $I =<a, b\,>$) we have

$$A(I) = A(<0, b\,>) \setminus A(<0, a)) \in D_\mu$$

and $\mu(A(I)) = b - a$. Analogously we can prove b). If we consider that for $x \in\, <0, 1)$ it holds $A(\{x\}) = A(<0, x]) - A(<0, x))$ we obtain it immediately.

Corollary 1. If y_n is B.u.d then, $\forall x \in\, <0, 1)$ we have $\mu(A(\{x\})) = 0$ (and $A(\{x\}) \in \mathcal{D}_\mu$).

Proposition 2. Let $\{y_n\}$ be a sequence of numbers from $<0, 1)$. Then $\{y_n\}$ is B.u.d if and only if $\mu^*(A(I)) = |I|$ for every subinterval $I \subset\, <0, 1)$.

Proof. One implication is trivial. Implication $\Longleftarrow$. Consider $I =<0, x)$, $J =<x, 1)$. Then $\mu^*(A(<0, x))) = x$, $\mu^*(A(<x, 1))) = 1 - x$ and so $A(<0, x)) \in D_\mu$ and the assertion follows now from Proposition 1 a).

Proposition 3. Let $E \subset\, <0, 1)$ be a dense set and $\{y_n\}$ a sequence of numbers from $<0, 1)$. The sequence $\{y_n\}$ is B.u.d if and only if
a) $\forall x \in E; \; A(<0, x)) \in D_\mu \wedge \mu(A(<0, x))) = x$
b) $\forall x \in E; \; A(<0, x\,>) \in D_\mu \wedge \mu(A(<0, x\,>)) = x$
c) For every interval $I \subset\, <0, 1)$, which endpoints belong to E, it holds $A(I) \in D_\mu$ and $\mu(A(I)) = |I|$.

Proof. Let x_0 be an arbitrary number from $<0, 1)$. Then there exist $x_1, x_2 \in E$ that $x_1 < x_0 < x_2$ and $x_2 - x_1 < \varepsilon$ (for $\varepsilon > 0$). And so $A(<0, x_1)) \subseteq A(<0, x_0)) \subseteq A(<0, x_2))$ and $A(<0, x_1\,>) \subseteq A(<0, x_0)) \subseteq A(<0, x_2\,>)$. Thus from (ii) we have that $A(<0, x_0)) \in D_\mu$ and the assertion follows in the cases a) and b). c) is trivial.

The sequence of Van der Corput

Let $q_0 = 1, q_1, q_2, \ldots$ be a sequence of positive integers that $q_j > 1$ for $j > 1$. Put

$$Q_n = q_0 \ldots q_n, n = 0, 1, 2, \ldots. \tag{5}$$

It is well known that every positive integer a can be uniquely expressed in the form

$$a = c_0 Q_0 + c_1 Q_1 + \cdots + c_n Q_n, \tag{6}$$

where $0 \leq c_j < q_{j+1}, j = 0, \ldots, n-1$. Similarly every $\alpha \in < 0, 1)$ can be uniquely expressed in the form

$$\alpha = \sum_{n=0}^{\infty} \frac{c_n}{Q_{n+1}}, \qquad 0 \leq c_n < q_{n+1} \tag{7}$$

and $c_n < q_{n+1} - 1$ for infinitely many n. If $a \in \mathbb{N}$ has the form (6), put

$$\gamma(a) = \frac{c_0}{Q_1} + \cdots + \frac{c_n}{Q_{n+1}}. \tag{8}$$

If $q_1 = q_2 = \ldots b, b$ for some $b \in \mathbb{N}, b > 1$, we obtain the classical Van der Corput sequence with the base b (see [D-T] p. 41, 368, [?]). Remark that this sequence plays an important role in the theory of Discrepancy.

Theorem 1. If $\{\gamma(k)\}$ is given by (8), then $\{\gamma(k)\}$ is B.u.d sequence.

Proof. For the proof we shall use some elementary properties of Cantor's expansions. Consider the intervals

$$I_{k+1}^j = \left\langle \frac{j}{Q_{k+1}}, \frac{j+1}{Q_{k+1}} \right), \qquad j = 0, \ldots, Q_{k+1} - 1, \ k = 0, \ldots.$$

Clearly the endpoints of these intervals form a dense set in $[0, 1)$. Thus Proposition 3 c) guaranties that it suffices to prove

$$\mu^*(A(I_{k+1}^j)) = \frac{1}{Q_{k+1}}. \tag{9}$$

To interval I_{k+1}^j we can uniquely associate a finite sequence $\bar{c}_0, \ldots, \bar{c}_k, 0 \leq \bar{c}_s < q_{s+1}$, $s = 0, \ldots, k$ that $\alpha \in I_{k+1}^j$ if and only if $\alpha = \sum_{n=0}^{\infty} \frac{c_n}{Q_{n+1}}$ where $c_0 = \bar{c}_0, \ldots, c_k = \bar{c}_k$. Similarly there exists an arithmetic progression $r + (Q_{k+1})$ that $a \in r + (Q_{k+1})$ if and only if $a = c_0 Q_0 + \cdots + c_k Q_k + \ldots$ where $c_0 = \bar{c}_0, \ldots, c_k = \bar{c}_k$. Thus it follows

$$\gamma(a) \in I_{k+1}^j \iff a \in r + (Q_{k+1})$$

and so $A(I_{k+1}^j) = r + (Q_{k+1})$ which implies (9).

Let α be an irrational number. It is a well known statement that the sequence of fractional parts $\{\{n\alpha\}\}$ is uniformly distributed. We prove that this sequence is not B.u.d.

Theorem 2. Let α be an irrational number. Put $y_n = \{n\alpha\}$, $n = 1, 2, \ldots$. Then for every $x \in (0, 1)$ it holds

$$\mu^*(A(< 0, x))) = 1 = \mu^*(A(< x, 1]).$$

Proof. We recall the Proposition on page 32 where Oto Strauch [S] proved that for every proper subinterval I the set $A(I)$ does not contain an infinite arithmetic progression. Therefore the complement $\mathbb{N} \setminus A(I)$ has a nonempty intersection with every arithmetic progression. Thus $\mu^*(\mathbb{N} \setminus A(I)) = 1$ (see [PAS]). For $I =< 0, x)$, $I =< x, 1 >$ we obtain the assertion.

Buck's measurable sequences

Suppose that $\{x_n\}$ is a sequence of numbers from $[0, 1)$. This sequence is called *Buck's measurable* if and only if for every subinterval $I \subseteq < 0, 1)$ the set $A(\{x_n\}, I)$ belongs to the algebra D_μ.

Remark that similar generalization of Weyl's u.d. sequence was made by I. Schoenberg [Sch] in 1929. Thus $\{x_n\}$ is B.u.d if it is Buck's measurable and $\mu(A(\{x_n\}, I)) = |I|$.

In this part we derive some analogies of the well known Weyl's criterium. We shall use one statement from thee previous chapter.

Clearly for every $n = 1, 2, \ldots$ we have $\chi_I(x_n) = \chi_{A(I)}(n)$ and so from Theorem 6 of previous chapter we obtain:

Proposition 4. Suppose that $\{B_n\}$ is a complete sequence. Let $\{x_n\}$ be a sequence of numbers from $< 0, 1)$. Then $\{x_n\}$ is Buck's measurable if and only if for every interval $I \subseteq [0, 1)$ there exists a value $C(I)$ that

$$\lim_{n \to \infty} \frac{1}{B_n} \sum_{j=1}^{B_n} \chi_I(x_{k_j^{(n)}}) = C(I) \tag{10}$$

holds for arbitrary system of complete remainders systems $R_n = \{k_1^{(n)}, \ldots, k_{B_n}^{(n)}\}$ modulo $B_n, n = 1, 2, \ldots$. In addition in this case there holds $C(I) = \mu(A(I))$.

Let us turn back to the Theorem 7 of previous chapter. This statement we can express in the form: **A set $A \subset \mathbb{N}$ is if and only if**

$$\lim_{N \to \infty} \frac{1}{N} \sum_{n=1}^{N} \chi_A(k_n) = \mu^*(A)$$

for every sequence $\{k_n\}$ which is uniformly distributed in $\mathbb{Z}$. This yields

Proposition 4'. Let $\{x_n\}$ be a sequence of numbers from $< 0, 1)$. Then $\{x_n\}$ is Buck's measurable if and only if for every interval $I \subseteq [0, 1)$ there exists a value $C(I)$ that

$$\lim_{N \to \infty} \frac{1}{N} \sum_{j=1}^{N} \chi_I(x_{k_n}) = C(I) \tag{10'}$$

holds for arbitrary sequence $\{k_n\}$ which is uniformly distributed in $\mathbb{Z}$. In addition in this case there holds $C(I) = \mu(A(I))$.

As an immediate consequence we have

Corollary 2. a) The sequence $\{x_n\}$, $x_n \in\ <0,1)$ is B.u.d if and only if for every subinterval $I \subset\ <0,1)$ there holds

$$\lim_{n\to\infty} \frac{1}{B_n} \sum_{j=1}^{B_n} \chi_I(x_{k_j^{(n)}}) = |I|,$$

using the same notation as in Proposition 4.

b)The sequence $\{x_n\}$, $x_n \in\ <0,1)$ is B.u.d if and only if for every subinterval $I \subset\ <0,1)$

$$\lim_{N\to\infty} \frac{1}{N} \sum_{j=1}^{N} \chi_I(x_{k_n}) = |I| \tag{10'}$$

holds for arbitrary sequence $\{k_n\}$ which is uniformly distributed in $\mathbb{Z}$.

Corollary 2 implies that $\{x_n\}$ is B.u.d if and only if

$$\lim_{n\to\infty} \frac{1}{B_n} \sum_{j=1}^{B_n} g(x_{k_j^{(n)}}) = \int_0^1 g(x) \, \mathrm{d}x$$

holds for every step function $g = \sum_i c_i \chi_{I_i}$.

For every Riemannian integrable function $f :<0,1>\to (\infty,\infty)$ and $\varepsilon > 0$ there exist two steps functions g_1, g_2 that

$$g_1 < f < g_2, \qquad \int_0^1 (g_2(x) - g_1(x)) \, \mathrm{d}x < \varepsilon . \tag{12}$$

Thus we get

Theorem 3. a) Suppose the notation from Proposition 4. Then $\{x_n\}$ is B.u.d if and only if

$$\lim_{n\to\infty} \frac{1}{B_n} \sum_{j=1}^{B_n} f(x_{k_j^{(n)}}) = \int_0^1 f(x) \, \mathrm{d}x \tag{13}$$

for arbitrary Riemannian integrable function $f :<0,1>\to (-\infty,\infty)$.

b) The sequence $\{x_n\}$, $x_n \in\ <0,1)$ is B.u.d if and only if for every Riemannian integrable function $f : [0,1] \to (-\infty,\infty)$ the equality

$$\lim_{N\to\infty} \frac{1}{N} \sum_{j=1}^{N} f(x_{k_n}) = \int_0^1 f(x) \, \mathrm{d}x \tag{13'}$$

holds for arbitrary sequence $\{k_n\}$ which is uniformly distributed in $\mathbb{Z}$.

Every Riemannian integrable function can be approximated in the sense (12) by two continuous functions g_1, g_2 and so we get

Theorem 3'. Suppose the notation from Proposition 4. Then $\{x_n\}$ is B.u.d if and only if

$$\lim_{n\to\infty} \frac{1}{B_n} \sum_{j=1}^{B_n} f(x_{k_j^{(n)}}) = \int_0^1 f(x)\, \mathrm{d}x$$

for every continuous function $f : [0,1] \to (-\infty, \infty)$.

b) The sequence $\{x_n\}$, $x_n \in< 0,1)$ is B.u.d if and only if for every continuous function $f :< 0,1 >\to (-\infty, \infty)$ the equality

$$\lim_{N\to\infty} \frac{1}{N} \sum_{j=1}^{N} f(x_{k_n}) = \int_0^1 f(x)\, \mathrm{d}x \tag{13'}$$

holds for arbitrary sequence $\{k_n\}$ which is uniformly distributed in $\mathbb{Z}$.

Every continuous function with same values in then endpoints of interval can be uniformly approximated by trigonometric polynomials and so it holds analogy to Weyl's criterion :

Theorem 4. a) Suppose the notation from Proposition 4. Then $\{x_n\}$ is B.u.d if and only if

$$\lim_{n\to\infty} \frac{1}{B_n} \sum_{j=0}^{B_n} \exp 2\pi\, \mathrm{i}\, h x_{k_j^{(n)}} = 0$$

for every $h \in \mathbb{Z}$, $h \neq 0$.

b) A sequence $\{x_n\}$ of elements of $< 0,1)$ is B.u.d if and only if

$$\lim_{N\to\infty} \frac{1}{N} \sum_{j=1}^{N} \exp 2\pi\, \mathrm{i}\, h x_{k_n} = 0 \tag{13'}$$

holds for arbitrary sequence $\{k_n\}$ which is uniformly distributed in $\mathbb{Z}$.

This yields

Corollary 3. A sequence $\{x_n\}$ of elements of $< 0,1)$ is B.u.d if and only if for arbitrary sequence $\{k_n\}$ which is uniformly distributed in $\mathbb{Z}$ is the sequence $\{x_{k_n}\}$ uniformly distributed.

Corollary 4. If $\{x_n\}$ is B.u.d, then the sequence of fractionals parts $\{\{kx_n\}\}$ is B.u.d for $k \in \mathbb{Z}$, $k \neq 0$.

A sequence $\{x_n\}$ is called *polyadically continuous* if and only if $\forall \varepsilon > 0$ there exists $B \in \mathbb{N}$ that

$$n \equiv m \quad (\mathrm{mod}\ B) \implies |x_n - x_m| < \varepsilon. \tag{14}$$

(We recall this notion from page 31.)

Theorem 5. Every u.d. sequence which is polyadically continuous is B.u.d

Proof. Let $\{x_n\}$ be a u.d. sequence. Then for every continuous function f there holds

$$\lim_{N\to\infty} \frac{1}{N} \sum_{n=1}^{N} f(x_n) = \int_0^1 f(x)\, \mathrm{d}x.$$

Suppose that a sequence $\{B_n\}$ fulfills the condition (c) of theorem A. Clearly

$$\int_0^1 f(x) \, dx = \lim_{n \to \infty} \frac{1}{B_n} \sum_{j=1}^{B_n} f(x_j).$$

If $R_n = \{k_1^{(n)}, \ldots, k_{B_n}^{(n)}\}$ is a complete remainder system modulo B_n, we can suppose that $j \equiv k_j^{(n)} (\bmod B_n), j = 1, \ldots, B_n$. If $\{x_n\}$ is polyadically continuous, then $\{f(x_n)\}$ is also polyadically continuous, because f is uniformly continuous. Let $\varepsilon > 0$ and B be from (14). Then from (c) we have $B | B_n, n \geq n_0$ for suitable n_0, hence $|f(x_j) - f(x_{k_j^{(n)}})| < \varepsilon$. And so

$$\left| \frac{1}{B_n} \sum_{j=1}^{B_n} f(x_j) - \frac{1}{B_n} \sum_{j=1}^{B_n} f(x_{k_j^{(n)}}) \right| < \varepsilon$$

for $n \geq n_0$. For $n \to \infty$ we have

$$\left| \int_0^1 f(x) \, dx - \limsup_{n \to \infty} \frac{1}{B_n} \sum_{j=1}^{B_n} f(x_{k_j^{(n)}}) \right| \leq \varepsilon$$

$$\left| \int_0^1 f(x) \, dx - \liminf_{n \to \infty} \frac{1}{B_n} \sum_{j=1}^{B_n} f(x_{k_j^{(n)}}) \right| \leq \varepsilon$$

and the assertion follows. □

Let us remark that Theorem 5 follows also from Proposition E on the page 50, considering the fact that for a function f continuous on the interval $< 0, 1 >$ and polyadically continuous sequence $\{x_n\}$ is the arithmetic function, $g(n) = f(x_n), n \in \mathbb{N}$ polyadically continuous.

If we consider the sequence of Van der Corput $\{\gamma(a)\}$ given by (8), then for $a_1 \equiv a_2$ $(\bmod Q_n)$ we have that a_1, a_2 have the same first n digits in (6) and so $|\gamma(a_1) - \gamma(a_2)| \leq Q_n^{-1}$. Therefore $\{\gamma(a)\}$ is an example of polyadically continuous sequence.

If $\{x_n\}$ is a Buck's measurable sequence, then the function

$$g(x) = \mu\big(A(\{x_n\}, < 0, x))\big) \tag{15}$$

is called the *Buck's distribution function* of $\{x_n\}$. Remark that for the asymptotic density in 1929 Schoenberg introduced the notion of *asymptotic distribution function* as $g(x) = d\big(A(\{x_n\}, < 0, x)\big)$ (see [Sch], [K-N], [D-T], [S-P]).

Let $g :< 0, 1 > \to < 0, 1 >$, $g(0) = 0$, $g(1) = 1$ be an increasing and continuous function. Then $g^{-1} :< 0, 1 > \to < 0, 1 >$ is also increasing and continuous. Consider the Van der Corput sequence $\{\gamma(n)\}$. Put $x_n = g^{-1}(\gamma(n))$, $n = 1, 2, \ldots$. Then $\{x_n\}$ is polyadically continuous, because $\{\gamma(n)\}$ is polyadically continuous. Moreover, for $x \in< 0, 1)$ we have

$$x_n < x \iff \gamma(n) < g(x),$$

thus g and $\{x_n\}$ fulfil ((15)). We proved

Proposition 5. If $g : [0, 1] \to [0, 1]$, $g(0) = 0$, $g(1) = 1$ **is an increasing and continuous function, then** $\{x_n\}$, **where** $x_n = g^{-1}(\gamma(n))$, **is a polyadically continuous sequence with Buck's distribution function** g.

For the case of the asymptotic density it holds stronger results (see [K-N],[D-T]).

Proposition 4 yields that if $\{x_n\}$ is Buck's measurable, then

$$\lim_{n \to \infty} \frac{1}{B_n} \sum_{j=1}^{B_n} h(x_{k_j^{(n)}}) = \int_0^1 h(x) \, dg(x)$$

for every step function h, where $g(x) = \mu(A < 0, x)$. As every continuous function f can be approximated in the sense (12) (instead of Riemann integral we consider Riemann-Stieltjes integral with respect to $g(x) = \mu(A(< 0, x)))$ we obtain

Theorem 6. Suppose the notation from Proposition 4. a)If $\{x_n\}$ **is Buck's measurable then, for every continuous function** $f :< 0, 1 > \to (-\infty, \infty)$ **it holds**

$$\lim_{n \to \infty} \frac{1}{B_n} \sum_{j=1}^{B_n} f(x_{k_j^{(n)}}) = \int_0^1 f(x) \, dg(x), \qquad (e)$$

where $g(x)$ **is the Buck's distribution function of** $\{x_n\}$.

b) Let $g(x)$ **be a continuous, non decreasing function defined on** $[0, 1]$ **and** $g(0) = 0$, $g(1) = 1$. **Then** $g(x)$ **is the Buck's distribution function of** $\{x_n\}$ **if and only if (e) holds.**

Part b) follows from the fact that in the case that $g(x)$ is continuous, every step function can be approximated by two continuous functions in the sense (12) (See [K-N] page 60, proof of the criterium for asymptotic distribution functions).

Analogously to Theorem 5, we can prove

Corollary 5. If $\{x_n\}$ **is a polyadically continuous sequence with continuous asymptotic distribution function, then** $\{x_n\}$ **is Buck's measurable**.

Now we can construct Buck's measurable sequences, using some results about multiplicative functions. Suppose that to a prime number p a positive value a_p is associated that the series $\sum a_p$ converges. Then the sequence $x_n = \prod_{p|n}(1 - a_p)$ is a sequence with a continuous asymptotic distribution function(see [E] page 185), and it can be easily proved that $\{x_n\}$ is polyadically continuous. Thus Corollary 5 yields that $\{x_n\}$ is Buck's measurable.

Some metric properties

Denote by B the set of all B.u.d sequences and by U the set of all u.d. sequences. The property (iii) yields that $B \subset U$.

Theorem 7. The set B **is closed with respect to the supremum metric**

Proof. Let $\{x_n\} \in \overline{B}$ — closure of B to the supremum metric. Then for $\varepsilon > 0$ there exists $\{y_n\} \in B$ that $|x_n - y_n| < \varepsilon$, $n = 1, 2, \dots$. If R_n is the system from P Proposition 4, we have

$$\left| \frac{1}{B_n} \sum_{j=1}^{B_n} \exp 2\pi i h x_{k_j^{(n)}} - \frac{1}{B_n} \sum_{j=1}^{B_n} \exp 2\pi i h y_{k_j^{(n)}} \right| \leq$$

$$\leq \frac{1}{B_n} \sum_{j=1}^{B_n} |\ldots| \leq 2\pi h \left| x_{k_j^{(n)}} - y_{k_j^{(n)}} \right| \leq 2\pi h \varepsilon.$$

For $\varepsilon \to 0^+$ we get, using Theorem 4, that

$$\lim_{n\to\infty} \frac{1}{B_n} \sum_{j=1}^{B_n} \exp 2\pi i h x_{k_j^{(n)}} = 0$$

for $h \neq 0$, $h \in Z$. And the assertion follows.   □

It is a well known fact that $\lambda^\infty(U) = 1$, where λ^∞ is a product measure on $< 0, 1)^\infty$ (see [K-N]).

Let $A \subset \mathbb{N}$. If there exists $\lim_{N\to\infty} \frac{1}{N} card(A \cap < k, k+N >)$ uniformly with respect to $k \in \mathbb{N}$ then its value is called the *uniform density* of A ($= u(A)$). (cf. [GLS], Theorem 1.1, Theorem 1.2). A sequence $\{y_n\}$, $y_n \in [0, 1)$ is called *well distributed* if and only if $u(A(\{y_n\}, I)) = |I|$ for every interval $I \subset\subset 0, 1 >$ (cf. [K-N], page 51). Every set $A \in D_\mu$ has a uniform density $u(A)$ and $u(A) = \mu(A)$. Thus every B.u.d. sequence is well distributed. The product measure of the set of well distributed sequences is 0 (see [K-N] Theorem 3.8, page 201). Thus $\lambda^\infty(B) = 0$. Theorem 2 gives also the example of sequence which is well distributed but no B.u.d (cf. [K-N] Example 5.2, page 42).

The theorem of John von Neumann

John von Neumann proved that every dense sequence in $(0, 1)$ can be rearranged to a u.d. sequence. We prove this result for B.u.d. sequence.

Directly from Theorem 4 we obtain:

Proposition 6. Let $\{y_n\}$ be a B.u.d.. sequence and $|x_n - y_n| \to 0$ as $n \to \infty$. **Then** $\{x_n\}$ is B.u.d.

Proposition 7. Let $\{y_n\}$ be a B.u.d. sequence and $\{x_n\}$ be such that $x_n = y_n$, for $n \in A$, where $A \in D_\mu$ and $\mu(A) = 1$. Then $\{x_n\}$ is B.u.d.

Proof.

$$\left| \frac{1}{B_n} \sum_{j=1}^{B_n} \exp 2\pi i h y_{k_j^{(n)}} - \frac{1}{B_n} \sum_{j=1}^{B_n} \exp 2\pi h i x_{k_j^{(n)}} \right|$$

$$\leq \frac{1}{B_n} \sum_{j \leq B_n, k_j^{(n)} \in \neg A} \left| \exp 2\pi i h x_{k_j^{(n)}} - \exp 2\pi i h y_{k_j^{(n)}} \right|$$

$$\leq \frac{2}{B_n} R(\neg A : B_n).$$

But $\mu(\neg A) = 1 - \mu(A) = 0$, we have

$$\lim_{n\to\infty} \frac{2}{B_n} R(\neg A : B_n) = 0$$

and the assertion follows from Theorem 4.

Theorem 8. Every sequence $\{x_n\}$ dense in $< 0, 1)$ can be rearranged to a B.u.d. sequence.

Proof. Consider the sequence $\{\gamma(n)\}$ of Van der Corput. This is a B.u.d. sequence (see Theorem 1). As $\{x_n\}$ is dense, for $n = 1, 2 \ldots$ there exists k_n that $\left| x_{k_n} - \gamma(n) \right| < \frac{1}{n}$. And so Proposition 5 yields that $\{x_{k_n}\}$ is a B.u.d. Let $\{x_{k'_n}\}$ be the sequence of elements of $\{x_n\}$ which do not occur in $\{x_{k_n}\}$. If $\{x_{k'_n}\}$ is finite, the proof is finished. Let $\{x_{k'_n}\}$ be infinite. Let $A \subseteq \mathbb{N}$ be such infinite set that $\mu(A) = 0$. For instance $A = \{n!;\ n = 1, 2, \ldots\}$.

Then $B = \mathbb{N} \setminus A \in D_\mu$ and $\mu(B) = 1$. Define the sequence $\{z_n\}$ as follows:

$$z_n = x_{k_n};\qquad n \in B.$$

Let $A = \{s_1 < s_2 < \ldots\}$, then

$$z_{s_{2j}} = x_{k'_j},\ j = 1, 2, \ldots$$

$$z_{s_{2j+1}} = x_{k_{s_j}} \cdot j = 1, 2, \ldots$$

Then $\{z_n\}$ is a rearrangement of $\{x_n\}$ and Proposition 6 yields $\{z_n\}$ is B.u.d.

The B.u.d. preserving mapping

In the paper [PSŠ] the mapping $g :< 0, 1 > \rightarrow < 0, 1 >$, that $\{g(y_n)\}$ is u.d., if $\{y_n\}$ u.d. is studied. Such mapping is called *u.d. preserving*. In this paper it is proved, that if g is Riemannian integrable, then g is u.d. preserving if and only if

$$\int_0^1 h(g(x))\ \mathrm{d}x = \int_0^1 h(x)\ \mathrm{d}x \tag{16}$$

holds for every continuous function $h :< 0, 1 > \rightarrow (-\infty, \infty)$.

A mapping $g :< 0, 1 > \rightarrow < 0, 1 >$ is called *B.u.d. preserving* if for every B.u.d. sequence $\{y_n\}$ is $\{g(y_n)\}$ B.u.d.

Theorem 9. A Riemannian integrable function $g :< 0, 1 > \rightarrow < 0, 1 >$ is B.u.d. preserving if and only if (16) holds for every continuous function $h :< 0, 1 > \rightarrow (-\infty, \infty)$.

Proof. In the third part we proved that $\{y_n\}$ is B.u.d. if and only if

$$\lim_{n \to \infty} \sum_{j=1}^{B_n} h(y_{k_j(n)}) = \int_0^1 h(x)\ \mathrm{d}x$$

(see the notation of Proposition 4). If we consider that both sequences $\{y_n\}$, $\{g(y_n)\}$ are B.u.d., then using the standard procedure from [PSŠ] we obtain the assertion.

Corollary 6. If $g :< 0, 1 > \rightarrow < 0, 1 >$ is a continuous function, fulfilling (16) then the sequence $\{g(\gamma(n))\}$ is a polyadically continuous B.u.d. sequence.

Permutations preserving the Buck's measure density

Now we shall go on with the study of the permutations $\mathbb{N} \to \mathbb{N}$ and theirs connections with density. Following notion will be the object observations: Let $g : \mathbb{N} \to \mathbb{N}$ be a permutation that

i) $\forall S \in \mathcal{D}_\mu; \ g(S) \in \mathcal{D}_\mu,$

ii) $\forall S \in \mathcal{D}_\mu; \ \mu(g(S)) = \mu(S),$

then we say that g *preserves Buck's measure density*.

We start with the proofs of some criterions and we give an example that these permutations do not form a group.

We recall Theorem 7 on the page 51. This theorem characterizes measurability by the uniform distribution in $\mathbb{Z}$. We use this result for the characterization of the preserving Buck's measure density.

Theorem 1. Let $g : \mathbb{N} \to \mathbb{N}$ be a permutation. Then following conditions are equivalent

(a) g **preserves Buck's measure density.**

(b) **For every sequence $\{x_n\}$ of positive integers which is uniformly distributed in $\mathbb{Z}$ is the sequence $\{g^{-1}(x_n)\}$ also uniformly distributed in $\mathbb{Z}$.**

Proof. Clearly, for every $S \subset \mathbb{N}$ and $x \in \mathbb{N}$ we have

$$x \in g(S) \iff g^{-1}(x) \in S,$$

thus $A(\{x_n\}, g(S)) = A(\{g^{-1}(x_n)\}, S)$. Therefore the implication $(a) \Rightarrow (b)$ is trivial. Let (b) holds, then for every $S \in \mathcal{D}_\mu$ and sequence $\{x_n\}$ of positive integers which is uniformly distributed in $\mathbb{Z}$ we have $d(A(\{x_n\}, g(S)) = \mu(S)$, thus Theorem 7, page 51, implies that $g(S) \in \mathcal{D}_\mu$ and $\mu(g(S)) = \mu(S)$. $\qquad \square$

Next result will have crucial rule for our following considerations:

Theorem 2. Let $g : \mathbb{N} \to \mathbb{N}$ be a permutation. The following properties are equivalent

a) g **preserves Buck's measure density.**

b) **For $A \subseteq \mathbb{N}$ it holds that $\mu^*(g(A)) \leq \mu^*(A)$.**

c) **For every arithmetic progression $a + (m)$, $a, m \in \mathbb{N}$, $m \neq 0$, it holds that $\mu^*(g(a + (m))) \leq \frac{1}{m}$.**

Proof. We prove b)$\Rightarrow$ a).Let b) holds. Then for $A \subseteq \mathcal{D}_\mu$ we have $\mathbb{N} \setminus g(A) = g(\mathbb{N} \setminus A)$ and so $1 \leq \mu^*(g(A)) + \mu^*(\mathbb{N} \setminus g(A)) \leq \mu^*(A) + \mu^*(\mathbb{N} \setminus A) = 1$ thus $g(A) \in \mathcal{D}_\mu$ and $\mu^*(A) = \mu^*(g(A))$.

The implication a)$\Rightarrow$ b). Let g preserves Buck's measure density. Then $\mu^*(g(a + (m))) = \frac{1}{m}$. For $A \subseteq \mathbb{N}$ and $\varepsilon > 0$ there exists such arithmetic progressions $a_1 + (m_1), \ldots, a_s + (m_s)$ that

$$A \subseteq (a_1 + (m_1)) \cup \cdots \cup (a_s + (m_s)) \tag{1}$$

and

$$\sum_{i=1}^{s} \frac{1}{m_i} \leq \mu^*(A) + \varepsilon. \tag{2}$$

From (1) we obtain

$$g(A) \subset g(a_1 + (m_1)) \cup \cdots \cup g(a_s + (m_s))$$

and so

$$\mu^*(g(A)) \leq \sum_{i=1}^{s} \frac{1}{m_i} \leq \mu^*(A) + \varepsilon.$$

For $\varepsilon \to 0^+$ we obtain $\mu^*(g(A)) \leq \mu^*(A)$.

a) $\Leftrightarrow$ c): If g preserves Buck's measure density, then c) holds.

If c) holds, then we can consider the covering (1) and (2). We obtain $\mu^*(g(A)) \leq \mu^*(A)$, thus g preserves Bucks's measure density. $\qquad\square$

Let S be the set of all permutations $\mathbb{N} \to \mathbb{N}$ which preserve Buck's measure density. Clearly S contains the identical permutation and Theorem 2 implies that with two permutations S contains its composition. Thus S is a semigroup with identity.

Example 1. If for some permutation g the value $|g(n) - n|$ is bounded then g belongs to G and so it preserves the asymptotic density. The following example shows that this is not true for the case of Buck's measure density.

Let $A = \{k+k!; k = 2, 3, ...\}$. For $m \geq 2, 0 \leq a < m$ it holds $(m+a)+(m+a)! \in a+m\mathbb{N}$ thus A has non empty intersection with every arithmetic progression and so (3) yields $\mu^*(A) = 1$(see [PAS]). Let the permutation $g : \mathbb{N} \to \mathbb{N}$ be defined as follows:$g(2n+(2n+1)!) = 2n+1+(2n + 1)!$, $g(2n + 1 + (2n + 1)!) = 2n + (2n + 1)!)$ and $g(a) = a$ in other cases. Consider now the set $B = \{2n + (2n + 1)!, 2n + (2n)!, ; n = 1, 2, ...\}$. Clearly it holds $B \subset (2)$ and so $\mu^*(B) \leq \frac{1}{2}$. But $g(B) = A$ thus Theorem 2 a) yields that g does not preserve the Buck's measure density. Trivially we have that $|g(n) - n| \leq 1$.

Now we give an example which shows that S is not a group.

Example 2. Let P be the set of all prime numbers. In the second part is proved that $\mu(P) = 0$. Let $A = \{a + a!; a \in \mathbb{N} \setminus P\}$ and $B = \mathbb{N} \setminus A = \{b_1 < b_2 < ...\}$. Let us consider arbitrary arithmetic progression $r + (m)$. This set contains some number $r + mk$ which is not a prime. Then the number $r + mk + (r + mk)!$ belongs to the intersection $(r + (m)) \cap A$. Thus A has the nonempty intersection with arbitrary arithmetic progression thus $\mu^*(A) = 1$. But the asymptotic density of A is zero thus the asymptotic density of B is 1, and so $\mu^*(B) = 1$. Therefore we have $A, B \notin \mathcal{D}_\mu$. Define $g : \mathbb{N} \to \mathbb{N}$ as follows: $g(B) = P$ and g is one to one on B and $g(a + a!) = a, a \notin P$. Then $g(A) = \mathbb{N} \setminus P$ and g is one to one on A. Consider now an arithmetic progression $r + (m)$. Then for $a \geq m$ $a + a! \equiv r \pmod{m}$if and only is $a \equiv r \pmod{m}$. (Recall the symbol $\simeq$ from the footnote at page 38.) We see that $A \cap (r + m\mathbb{N}) \simeq \{(r + ms) + (r + ms)!; s = 1, 2, ..., \wedge r + ms \notin P\}$. And so $g(A \cap (r+(m)) \simeq (r+m\mathbb{N}) \setminus P$. Moreover $g(B \cap (r+(m)) \subseteq P$ and so $\mu(g(B \cap (r+m\mathbb{N})) = 0$, thus $\mu^*(g(r + (m)) = \frac{1}{m}$. From Theorem 2 we get that g preserves Buck's measure density. But evidently $g^{-1}(P) = B$ and so g^{-1} does not preserve Buck's measure density.

a) **If we consider in Example 2 all possibilities of bijective mapping $g(B) = P$ we obtain that the cardinality of S is continuum.**

b) **Theorem 2 yields immediately that $g, g^{-1} \in S$ if and only if $\mu^*(g(A)) = \mu^*(A)$ for arbitrary an $A \subseteq \mathbb{N}$.**

Now we use Theorem 2 and (3) for the proof of the criterions in the limit form. Let $\{a(n)\}, \{b(n)\}$ be two sequences of positive integers. As usually we shall write $a(n) = o(b(n))$ if and only if $\frac{a(n)}{b(n)} \to 0$ for $n \to \infty$.

Corollary. Suppose that $\{B_n\}$ is a complete sequence. Then for a permutation $g : \mathbb{N} \to \mathbb{N}$ the following conditions are equivalen:

a) **g preserves Buck's measure density**

b) **for every $m \in \mathbb{N}, m \neq 0, a \in \mathbb{N}$ the set $g(a+m\mathbb{N})$ contains at most $\frac{B_n}{m}+o(B_n)$ elements incongruent modulo B_n where the therm $o(B_n)$ depends on m and a modulo m.**

Proof. a) $\implies$ b): Consider an arithmetic progression $a + (m), a, m \in \mathbb{N}, m \neq 0$. Denote by a' the rest of a after division by m. Then $a + (m) \subset a' + (m)$, therefore the set $g(a + (m))$ contains at most $R(g(a' + (m)) : B_n)$ elements incongruent modulo B_n. But (3) yields $R(g(a' + (m)) : B_n) = \mu^*(g(a' + (m)))B_n + o(B_n)$. And so Theorem 2 b) implies b).

b) $\implies$ a): From b) we deduce that $R(g(a+(m)) : B_n) \leq \frac{B_n}{m} + o(B_n)$. Now from Theorem 2 b) we obtain that g preserves Buck's measure density. $\qquad \square$

Theorem 3. Suppose that $\{B_n\}$ is a complete sequence. Then a permutation $g : \mathbb{N} \to \mathbb{N}$ preserves Buck's measure density if and only if for every $m \in \mathbb{N}, m \neq 0$, and arbitrary sequence of finite sets of positive integers $\{k_1^{(n)}, \ldots, k_{r(n)}^{(n)}\}, r(n) \geq 1, n = 1, 2, \ldots$ which are incongruent modulo B_n, the set of co-images $\{g^{-1}(k_1^{(n)}), \ldots, g^{-1}(k_{r(n)}^{(n)})\}$ contains at least

$$T_n = \frac{r(n)}{B_n} \cdot m + o(1) \tag{4}$$

elements incongruent modulo m, for $n = 1, 2, \ldots$.

Proof. Let g preserve the Buck's measure density. Let $g^{-1}(k_j^{(n)}) = l_j^{(n)}, j = 1, \ldots, r(n)$. Suppose that the numbers $l_j^{(n)}, j = 1, \ldots, r(n)$ contain W_n elements incongruent modulo m. Then these numbers belong to W_n arithmetic progressions $a_1 + (m), \ldots, a_s + (m), s = W_n$. By applying Corollary 1 to the arithmetic progression $a_j + m\mathbb{N}$ we obtain that the set $g(a_j + m\mathbb{N})$ contains at most $\frac{B_n}{m} + \delta_j(B_n)$ elements incongruent modulo B_n where $\delta_j(B_n) = o(B_n), j = 1, \ldots, s$. Therefore the sequence $k_j^{(n)} = g(l_j^{(n)}), j = 1, \ldots, r(n)$ contains at most $W_n \cdot \frac{B_n}{m} + \delta_1(B_n) + \cdots + \delta_s(B_n)$ elements incongruent modulo B_n. Clearly $1 \leq s = W_n \leq m$ thus $\delta_1(B_n) + \cdots + \delta_s(B_n) = o(B_n)$. Therefore $r(n) \leq W_n \cdot \frac{B_n}{m} + o(B_n) = W_n(\frac{B_n}{m} + o(B_n))$ and this implies

$$\frac{r(n)}{B_n} \cdot \left(\frac{1}{m} + o(1)\right)^{-1} \leq W_n.$$

By an easy calculation we get

$$\frac{r(n)}{B_n} \cdot \left(\frac{1}{m} + o(1)\right)^{-1} = \frac{r(n)}{B_n} \cdot m + o(1).$$

Let us suppose that (4) holds. Let $g(a+ms_1), \ldots, g(a+ms_{r(n)})$, $s_j \in \mathbb{N}$ for $j = 1, \ldots, r(n)$ be the representatives of $g(a + (m))$ module B_n. Then these numbers are incongruent modulo B_n and $r(n) = R(g(a+m\mathbb{N}) : B_n)$. From (4) we see that the sequence $a+ms_1, \ldots, a+ms_{r(n)}$ contains at least T_n elements incongruent modulo m, but it contains only 1 element incongruent modulo m, thus

$$\frac{r(n)}{B_n} \cdot m + o(1) \leq 1$$

and so

$$\frac{r(n)}{B_n} \leq \frac{1 + o(1)}{m}.$$

Therefore Theorem 5, page 46 yields that

$$\mu^*(g(a + (m))) = \lim_{n \to \infty} \frac{R(g(a + (m)) : B_n)}{B_n} \leq \frac{1}{m}.$$

Theorem 2 now implies that g preserves Buck's measure density.   □

Corollary. If g preserves Buck's measure density then for every $m \in \mathbb{N}$, $m \neq 1$ and every sequence of complete remainder systems modulo B_n, $n = 1, 2, \ldots$ $k_1^{(n)}, \ldots, k_{B_n}^{(n)}$ the sequence $g^{-1}(k_1^{(n)}), \ldots, g^{-1}(k_{B_n}^{(n)})$ contains at least $\frac{m}{1+o(1)}$ elements incongruent modulo m.

Lemma. Let $A \subset \mathbb{N}$ and $m, B \in \mathbb{N}$ and $m|B$. Then

$$R(A : m) \geq \frac{R(A : B)}{B} m .$$

Proof: Put $s = R(A : m)$. Then for suitable $a_1, \ldots, a_s$ there holds

$$A \subset \bigcup_{i=1}^{s} a_i + (m).$$

For every i we have $a_i + (m) = \cup_{j=1}^{\frac{B}{m}-1} a_i + jm + (B)$. This implies that A is subset of union of $s\frac{B}{m}$ arithmetic progressions of the form $b + (B)$ therefore $R(A : B) \leq s\frac{B}{m}$.   □

Using Theorem 3 we can make an other proof that the mapping g from Example 2 preserves Buck's measure density : Let us consider arbitrary system $\{k_1^{(n)}, \ldots, k_{r(n)}^{(n)}\}$ of incongruent numbers modulo B_n, $r(n) \geq 1$, $n = 1, \ldots$. Let $m \in \mathbb{N}$, each of these sets contains at least $r(n) - m - R(P, B_n) = r(n) + o(B_n)$ elements greater than m which are not primes. Lemma yields that these numbers contain at least $\frac{r(n)+o(B_n)}{B_n}m = \frac{r(n)}{B_n}m + o(1)$ elements incongruent modulo m. From the formula formula for g we see that also theirs co images are incongruent modulo m.

$$* * *$$

In this part we construct sufficiently small set, countable, of permutations which preserve Buck's measure density, but which is sufficiently rich from the ergodic point of view (Theorem 5). We shall use the following:

Theorem 4. Suppose that $\{B_n\}$ is a complete sequence. Let $g : \mathbb{N} \to \mathbb{N}$ be such a permutation that for every sequence of complete remainder systems $\{k_1^{(n)}, \ldots, k_{B_n}^{(n)}\}$ modulo B_n, the set of the co - images $\{g^{-1}(k_1^{(n)}), \ldots, g^{-1}(k_{B_n}^{(n)})\}$ contains at least $\frac{B_n}{1+o(1)}$ elements incongruent modulo B_n, $n = 1, 2, \ldots$. Then g preserves Buck's measure density.

Proof. Let $A \subseteq \mathbb{N}$ and let $g(l_1^{(n)}), \ldots, g(l_{r(n)}^{(n)})$, for $l_j^{(n)} \in A$, are incongruent modulo B_n. Then this sequence can be completed to build the complete remainder system modulo B_n, by the elements $g(l_j^{(n)})$, $j = r(n) + 1, \ldots, B_n$. Thus $l_1^{(n)}, \ldots, l_{r(n)}^{(n)}, l_{r(n)+1}^{(n)}, \ldots, l_{B_n}^{(n)}$ contains at least $\frac{B_n}{1+o(1)}$ elements incongruent modulo B_n.

Let $l_1^{(n)}, \ldots, l_{r(n)}^{(n)}$ contain at most $p(n)$ elements incongruent modulo B_n. Then

$$\frac{B_n}{1+o(1)} \leq p(n) + (B_n - r(n)),$$

and so

$$r(n) - p(n) \leq B_n \left(1 - \frac{1}{1+o(1)}\right),$$

therefore

$$\lim_{n \to \infty} \frac{r(n) - p(n)}{B_n} = 0. \tag{5}$$

Let $r(n) = R(g(A) : B_n)$, then A contains at least $p(n)$ elements incongruent modulo B_n and so

$$R(A : B_n) \geq p(n) = R(g(A) : B_n) + p(n) - r(n),$$

thus from Theorem 5, page 46 we have

$$\mu^*(A) \geq \mu^*(g(A))$$

and Theorem 2 implies the assertion. $\qquad\square$

Other proof of Theorem 4 can be made using Theorem 3:

Let $\{k_1^{(n)}, \ldots, k_{r(n)}^{(n)}\}$, $n = 1, \ldots$ be an arbitrary system of finite sequences of positive integers incongruent modulo B_n, $r(n) > 0$, $n = 1, \ldots 1$. Let m be positive integer. Suppose that the sequence $\{g^{-1}(k_1^{(n)}), \ldots, g^{-1}(k_{r(n)}^{(n)})\}$ of theirs co - images contains exactly s_n elements incongruent modulo m. Then

$$\{g^{-1}(k_1^{(n)}), \ldots, g^{-1}(k_{r(n)}^{(n)})\} \subset \bigcup_{i=1}^{s_n} a_i^n + (m) \tag{a}$$

for suitable non negative integers $a_i^n, i = 1, \ldots, s_n$. Let $m|B_n, n > n_0$. Then for $n > n_0$ the arithmetic progression $a_i^n + (m)$ contains $\frac{B_n}{m}$ elements incongruent modulo B_n. Thus from (a) we have that $\{g^{-1}(k_1^{(n)}), \ldots, g^{-1}(k_{r(n)}^{(n)})\}$ contains at most $s_n \frac{B_n}{m}$ elements incongruent modulo B_n. Let us complete these systems of incongruent numbers by suitable values $\{k_{r(n)+1}^{(n)}, \ldots, k_{B_n}^{(n)}\}$ to the complete reminder system s modulo B_n. Then the system of co - images

$$\{g^{-1}(k_1^{(n)}), \ldots, g^{-1}(k_{r(n)}^{(n)})\} \cup \{g^{-1}(k_{r(n)+1}^{(n)}), \ldots, g^{-1}(k_{B_n}^{(n)})\}$$

contains at most $\frac{B_n}{m} + B_n - r(n)$ elements incongruent modulo B_n, thus from the assumption we get

$$s_n \frac{B_n}{m} + B_n - r(n) \geq \frac{B_n}{1 + o(1)},$$

and so by easy transformation we get

$$s_n \geq \frac{r(n)}{B_n} m + o(1).$$

And the assertion follows from Theorem 3.   □

Now we construct a system of quite trivial permutations $g \in S$ such that $g^{-1} \in S$.

Proposition 1. Suppose that m is a positive integer. Let $Z_m = \{0, ..., m - 1\}$ and $\pi : Z_m \to Z_m$ a permutation. Then the mapping $g_\pi : \mathbb{N} \to \mathbb{N}$

$$g_\pi(a + jm) = \pi(a) + j \cdot m \tag{6}$$

is a permutation which preserves Buck's measure density.

Proof. It is trivial that g_π defined by (6) is a permutation. Suppose that $\{B_n\}$ is a sequence of positive integers which fulfils the condition (v) and $m | B_n, n = 1, \ldots$. Let $\{k_1^{(n)}, \ldots, k_{B_n}^{(n)}\}$ be a complete reminder system modulo B_n. Put $k_j^{(n)} = a_j + ml_j$. Then $g_\pi^{-1}(k_j^{(n)}) = \pi^{-1}(a_j) + ml_j$. If $g_\pi^{-1}(k_j^{(n)}) \equiv g_\pi^{-1}(k_i^{(n)}) \pmod{B_n}$, then $\pi^{-1}(a_j) + ml_j \equiv \pi^{-1}(a_i) + ml_i \pmod{B_n}$, and so $\pi^{-1}(a_j) \equiv \pi^{-1}(a_i) \pmod{m}$, thus $a_j = a_i$. Therefore $ml_j \equiv ml_i \pmod{B_n}$, this implies $k_j^{(n)} \equiv k_i^{(n)} \pmod{B_n}$ — contradiction. So Theorem 4 yields the assertion.   □

It is easy to see that the value $|g_\pi(n) - n|$ is bounded and so g_π preserves the asymptotic density. Moreover these permutations form a countable set.

Proposition 2. Let $A, B \in \mathcal{D}_\mu$ and $\mu(A) = \mu(B)$. Then for $\varepsilon > 0$ there exist the sets $A_1 \subseteq A$, $B_1 \subseteq B$, $A_1, B_1 \in \mathcal{D}_\mu$ such that $\mu(A) - \mu(A_1) < \varepsilon$ and $\mu(B) - \mu(B_1) < \varepsilon$ and a permutation g_π (given by (6)) that $g_\pi(A_1) = B_1$.

Proof. If $\mu(A) = 0 = \mu(B)$, we can consider $A_1 = \emptyset = B_1$ and g_π-identic permutation.

Suppose that $\mu(A) > 0$. Then from (iv) it follows that there exists $m \in \mathbb{N}$ and the $a_1, \ldots, a_s$, $b_1, \ldots, b_q \in \mathbb{N}$ that

$$(a_1 + (m)) \cup \cdots \cup (a_s + (m)) \subseteq A,$$

$$(b_1 + (m)) \cup \cdots \cup (b_q + (m)) \subseteq B$$

and $\mu(A) - \frac{s}{m} < \varepsilon, \mu(B) - \frac{q}{m} < \varepsilon$. Such as $\mu(A) = \mu(B)$ we can assume that $s = q$. If we now consider that $A_1 = \bigcup a_i + m\mathbb{N}$, $B_1 = \bigcup b_i + m\mathbb{N}$, and such a permutation π of complete reminder system modulo m that $\pi(a_i \pmod{m}) = b_i \pmod{m}$, then g_π satisfies the assertion.   □

Theorem 5. Let $A \in \mathcal{D}_\mu$ be such a set that

$$\mu(A \ominus g_\pi(A)) = 0 \tag{7}$$

($\ominus$ is the symmetric difference), for every permutation g_π given by (6). Then $\mu(A) = 1$ or $\mu(A) = 0$.

Proof. Suppose that $0 < \mu(A) < 1$. Clearly (7) holds also for $\mathbb{N} \setminus A$ and so we can suppose that $0 < \mu(A) \leq \frac{1}{2}, \frac{1}{2} \leq \mu(\mathbb{N} \setminus A) < 1$. The Darboux property of Buck's measure density (cf. [PAS]) implies that there exists a set $B \subset \mathbb{N} \setminus A$ that $\mu(B) = \mu(A)$. Let $\mu(A) > \varepsilon > 0$ and $A_1 \subset A$, $B_1 \subset B$ be the set from Proposition 6. Then $g_\pi(A_1) = B_1$ for suitable permutation g_π. Clearly

$$\mu(A \ominus g_\pi(A)) = \mu(A \setminus g_\pi(A)) + \mu(g_\pi(A) \setminus A).$$

Put $A = A_1 \cup \tilde{A}$ where $A_1 \cap \tilde{A} = \emptyset$, then $\tilde{A} \in D_\mu$ and $\mu(\tilde{A}) < \varepsilon$, thus

$$A \setminus g_\pi(A) = A \setminus g_\pi(A_1 \cup \tilde{A}) =$$

$$= A \setminus (g_\pi(A_1) \cup g(\tilde{A})) = A \setminus (B_1 \cup g_\pi(\tilde{A})) = A \setminus g_\pi(\tilde{A})$$

and so

$$\mu(A \setminus g_\pi(A)) = \mu(A) - \mu(g_\pi(\tilde{A})) \geq \mu(A) - \varepsilon$$

considering $\varepsilon < \frac{1}{2}\mu(A)$ we obtain $\mu(A \ominus g_\pi(A)) > 0$ — a contradiction. $\qquad\square$

* * *

As is quoted in first chapter it has been proved in [N-P] that that every permutation which preserves to have asymptotic density preserves also its value, (see Theorem A, page 23). We give an example that this does not hold for Buck's measurability. We construct a permutation $g : \mathbb{N} \to \mathbb{N}$ which preserves Buck's measurability but does not preserve Buck's measure density. Put

$$g(2n) = 4n,$$

$$g(4n + 1) = 4n + 2,$$

$$g(4n + 3) = 2n + 1$$

Clearly this mapping is a permutation $\mathbb{N} \to \mathbb{N}$. Consider now an arithmetic progression of the form $a + (4m)$.

Suppose that $2|a$. Then $a = 2a_1$, thus for $k \in a + (4m)$ we have $k + 2a_1 + 4m_j$, and so $g(k) = 4a_1 + 8m_j$, therefore it holds $g(a + (4m)) = 2a + 8m\mathbb{N}$.

Suppose now that $a \equiv 1 \pmod 4$. Then $a + (4m) = 1 + 4a_1 + (4m)$ and so for $k \in a + (4m)$ we have $k = 4a_1 + 1 + 4m_j$, thus $g(k) = 4a_1 + 2 + 4m_j$, therefore in this case $g(a + (4m)) = a + 1 + (4m)$.

Finally consider $a \equiv 3 \pmod 4$. Then for $k \in a + (4m)$ we have $k = 4a_1 + 3 + 4m_j$, and so $g(k) = 1 + 2a_1 + 2m_j$, thus $g(a + (4m)) = \frac{a-1}{2} + (2m)$.

Let $A \subseteq 3 + (4)$ be a Buck's measurable set. Then for $\varepsilon > 0$ there exists such $m \in \mathbb{N}$ and $a_1, \ldots, a_s, b_1, \ldots, b_r \in \mathbb{N}$ that $(a_1 + (4m)) \cup \cdots \cup (a_s + (4m)) \subseteq A \subseteq \bigcup_{i=1}^{r} (b_i + (4m))$ and $\frac{r-s}{4m} < \varepsilon$. Such as $A \subseteq 3 + (4)$ we can consider $a_i \equiv 3 \pmod 4$, $b_j \equiv 3 \pmod 4$.
Thus

$$\bigcup_{i=1}^{s} g(a_i + (4m)) \subseteq g(A) \subseteq \bigcup_{i=1}^{r} g(b_i + (4m)).$$

Clearly

$$\bigcup_{i=1}^{s} a_i' + (2m) \subseteq g(A) \subseteq \bigcup_{i=1}^{r} b_i' + (2m).$$

$$\left(a_i' = \frac{a_i - 1}{2}, \ b_i' = \frac{b_i - 1}{2} \right)$$

moreover

$$\frac{r - s}{2m} < 2\varepsilon$$

and so $g(A)$ is Buck's measurable set, and from the previous considerations it follows that $\mu(g(A)) = 2\mu(A)$.

Analogously we can prove that for $B \subseteq 1 + (4)$ the image $g(B)$ is Buck's measurable and $\mu(g(B)) = \mu(B)$, and for $C \subseteq (2)$ the set $g(C)$ is Buck's measurable, and $\mu(g(C)) = \frac{1}{2}\mu(C)$. If $S \subseteq \mathbb{N}$ is a Buck's measurable set then it can be represented in the form

$$S = A \cup B \cup C, \quad A \subseteq 3 + (4), \quad B \subseteq 1 + (4), \quad C \subseteq (2).$$

From (ii) it follows that the sets A, B, C are Buck's measurable and so $g(S) = g(A) \cup g(B) \cup g(C)$ is a Buck's measurable set. Similarly it can be proved that g^{-1} preserves Buck's measurability. It is easy to see that g does not preserve Buck's measure density.

Uniform density

The concept of the uniform density of sets of positive integers is based on the ratio of blocs and gaps in a certain set. It was the object of observations in [BF], where the set of exponents, which does not hold the Fermat last theorem, have been studied.

Let $A \subset \mathbb{N}$ and $x < y$ be two positive real number, put $A(x, y) := A(y) - A(x)$, this value gives us the number of elements of A between x, y.

Denote

$$\alpha^s(A) = \max_k A(k, k + s), \alpha_s(A) = \min_k A(k, k + s).$$

Clearly for arbitrary k, s_1, s_2 positive integers, there holds

$$A(k, k + s_1 + s_2) = A(k, k + s_1) + A(k + s_1, k + s_1 + s_2),$$

thus

$$\alpha^{s_1+s_2}(A) \leq \alpha^{s_1}(A) + \alpha^{s_2}(A), \quad \alpha_{s_1+s_2}(A) \geq \alpha_{s_1}(A) + \alpha_{s_2}(A).$$

Following lemma provides that there exist the limits $\lim_s \frac{1}{s}\alpha^s(A) := \overline{u}(A)$ and $\lim_s \frac{1}{s}\alpha_s(A) := \underline{u}(A)$.

Lemma.

a) **Let $\{a_n\}$ be a sequence of real numbers fulfilling the condition $a_{s_1+s_2} \leq a_{s_1} + a_{s_2}$ then $\inf_{s\in\mathbb{N}} \frac{a_s}{s} = \lim_{s\to\infty} \frac{a_s}{s}$.**

b) **Let $\{a_n\}$ be a sequence of real numbers fulfilling the condition $a_{s_1+s_2} \geq a_{s_1} + a_{s_2}$ then $\sup_{s\in\mathbb{N}} \frac{a_s}{s} = \lim_{s\to\infty} \frac{a_s}{s}$.**

Proof: Clearly a)⟺b). We prove a). Put $\iota = \inf_{s\in\mathbb{N}} \frac{a_s}{s}$. Suppose that $\iota > -\infty$. For $\varepsilon > 0$ there exists $m \in \mathbb{N}$ that $\iota \leq \frac{a_m}{m} \leq \iota + \varepsilon$. If $n > m$ then $n = km + r, 0 \leq r < m$. We get

$$\frac{a_n}{n} = \frac{a_{km+r}}{km+r} \leq \frac{ka_m + a_r}{km+r} \leq$$

$$\leq \frac{a_m}{m} + \frac{a_r}{km} \leq \iota + \varepsilon + \frac{a_r}{km}.$$

Let n be so great that for $k = [\frac{n}{m}]$ we have $\frac{a_r}{km} < \varepsilon, r = 1, ..., m - 1$. Then $\frac{a_n}{n} < \iota + 2\varepsilon$. The case $\iota = -\infty$ can be proved analogously. $\square$

This Lemma is originated by Fekete in [F].

Value $\overline{u}(A)$ is called the *upper uniform* density of A and the value $\underline{u}(A)$ is called the *lower uniform* density of A.

The definition implies:

i) **If $A \subset \mathbb{N}$ and the set A contains the blocks of consecutive numbers of arbitrary length then $\overline{u}(A) = 1$.** Let us denote $B = \mathbb{N} \setminus A$. Then $B(k, k + s) = s - A(k, k + s)$ thus $\underline{u}(B) = 1 - \overline{u}(A)$ and $\overline{u}(B) = 1 - \underline{u}(A)$. Therefore it holds.

ii) **If $A \subset \mathbb{N}$ and the set $\mathbb{N} \setminus A$ contains the blocks of consecutive numbers of arbitrary length then $\underline{u}(A) = 0$.**

Theorem 1.   Let A, B be two infinite subsets of $\mathbb{N}$ such that A contains the blocks of consecutive elements from B of arbitrary length. Then $\overline{u}(A) \geq \underline{u}(B)$.

Proof: The assumptions yield that for an arbitrary n, it is such k that $A(k, k+n) \geq B(k, k+n)$, thus $\max_k A(k, k+n) \geq \min_k B(k, k+n)$ and the assertion follows.   □

If for $A \subset \mathbb{N}$ it holds $\underline{u}(A) = \overline{u}(A) := u(A)$, then we say that A has *uniform density*, and the value $u(A)$ is called *the uniform density* of A.

There are some other definitions of this notion. We refer to [GTT].

Let $A = \{a_1 < a_2 < ...\}$ be an infinite set. It is well known fact that if $\sum_n a_n^{-1} < \infty$ then A has the asymptotic density and $d(A) = 0$. Now we give an example that this does not hold for the uniform density. Consider the set $A = \cup_n \{n! + 1, ..., n! + n\}$. From i) we see that $\overline{u}(A) = 1$ but it is easy to prove that in this case $\sum_n a_n^{-1} < \infty$.

Theorem 2.   Let $\{m_n\}$ be a sequence of positive integers, such that $(m_j, m_k) = 1$ for $k \neq j$. Put $A = \cup_{n=1}^{\infty}(m_n)$. Then
$$\overline{u}(A) = 1$$
$$\underline{u}(A) = 1 - \prod_{n=1}^{\infty}(1 - \tfrac{1}{m_n}).$$

Proof: (1). The numbers $m_1, ..., m_n$ are relatively prime, thus due to the Chinese reminder theorem, we obtain that there exists such a positive integer x_n that $x_n \equiv -j \pmod{m_j}$ for $j = 1, ..., n$. Therefore $x_n + j \in (m_j)$, j=1,...,n. This yields $x_n + 1, ..., x_n + n \in A$ and from i) we obtain $\overline{u}(A) = 1$.

(2).Put $A_n = \cup_{j=1}^{n}(m_j)$. Clearly $A_n \subset A$. It can be easily proven $u(A_n) = 1 - \prod_{j=1}^{n}(1 - \tfrac{1}{m_j})$ and so for $n \to \infty$ we obtain $1 - \prod_n(1 - \tfrac{1}{m_n}) \leq \underline{u}(A)$. Other inequality we obtain from the fact that $d(A) = 1 - \prod_{n=1}^{\infty}(1 - \tfrac{1}{m_n})$.   □

Denote by Q_n, for $n = 2, 3, ...$ the set of positive integers which are not divisible by the $n-$th power of prime number. Then it holds $\mathbb{N} \setminus Q_n = \cup(p^n)$, where the union is considered through all prime numbers p. Thus $\underline{u}(\mathbb{N} \setminus Q_n) = 1 - \prod(1 - p^{-n}) > 0$ and so from ii) it follows that Q_n does not contain the blocks of consecutive integers of arbitrary length.

Uniform density as uniform limit

In the paper [GLS], the following characterization of the sets having uniform density is proved:

Theorem 3. Let $A \subset \mathbb{N}$. Then A has uniform density if and only if for suitable L

$$\lim_{s \to \infty} \frac{A(t + 1, t + s)}{s} = L$$

uniformly with respect to $t \geq 0$. And in this case $L = u(A)$.

Proof: Let $\varepsilon > 0$. By this assumption, there exists a $s_0 = s_0(\varepsilon) \in N$ such that for each $s > s_0$ and each $t \geq 0$ we have

$$(L - \varepsilon)s < A(t + 1, t + s) < (L + \varepsilon)s.$$

By the definition of the numbers β_s, β^s we get from this for $s > s_0$

$$L - \varepsilon \leq \frac{\beta_s}{s} \leq \frac{\beta^s}{s} \leq L + \varepsilon.$$

If $s \to \infty$, we get

$$L - \varepsilon \leq \underline{u}(A) \leq \overline{u}(A) \leq L + \varepsilon.$$

Since $\varepsilon > 0$ is an arbitrary positive number, we get $u(A) = L$.

Put $u(A) = L$. Since

$$L = \lim_{p \to \infty} \frac{\alpha_p}{p} = \lim_{p \to \infty} \frac{\alpha^p}{p}$$

for every $\varepsilon > 0$, there exists a p_0 such that for each $p > p_0$ we have

$$(L - \varepsilon)p < \alpha_p \leq \alpha^p < (L + \varepsilon)p.$$

So we get

$$(L - \varepsilon)p < \min_{t \geq 0} A(t + 1, t + p) \leq \max_{t \geq 0} A(t + 1, t + p) < (L + \varepsilon)p.$$

By the definition of $A(t + 1, t + p)$ we get from this

$$\left| \frac{A(t + 1, t + p)}{p} - L \right| \leq \varepsilon$$

for each $p > p_0$ and each $t \geq 0$. Hence

$$\lim_{p \to \infty} \frac{A(t + 1, t + p)}{p} = L \qquad (= u(A))$$

uniformly with respect to $t \geq 0$. $\qquad\qquad\qquad\qquad\qquad\qquad\qquad\qquad\qquad\square$

Denote by $\mathcal{U}$ the system of sets having the uniform density. Theorem 3 guarantees that

$$\mathcal{D}_\mu \subset \mathcal{U}, \ \mu(S) = u(S), S \in \mathcal{D}. \qquad\qquad (*)$$

Now we shall study one type of arithmetic functions, from the point of view of the uniform density of their range. From Theorem 3, we derive the following condition when an arithmetic function, preserves uniform density 0.

Lemma 1. Let $f : \mathbb{N} \to \mathbb{N}$ be an arithmetic function, fulfilling the condition (a) $\liminf_{n \to \infty} \frac{f(n+k) - f(k)}{n} > 0$ **uniformly for $k = 1, 2, ...$**

Then for every $A \subset \mathbb{N}, u(A) = 0$ it holds $u(f(A)) = 0$.

Proof: The condition (a) implies that for a suitable $\beta > 0, n_0 \in \mathbb{N}$ we have

$$f(n + k) - f(k) \geq \beta n, \ n \geq n_0, \ k = 1, 2, ... \qquad\qquad (1)$$

Thus the set $F := f(\mathbb{N})$ can be represented in the form $F = F^{(1)} \cup \cdots \cup F^{(n_0)}$ where

$$F^{(i)} = \{f(i) < f(i + n_0) < ... < f(i + mn_0) < ...\},$$

for $i = 1, ..., n_0$. Let us denote $E^{(i)} = F^{(i)} \cap f(A)$. Thus $E^{(i)} = \{f(i + mn_0); i + mn_0 \in A, m \in \mathbb{N}\}, i = 1, ..., n_0$. Clearly $f(A) \subset E^{(1)} \cup ... \cup E^{(n_0)}$, therefore it suffices to prove $u(E^{(i)}) = 0, i = 1, ..., n_0$.

Let $k, n \in \mathbb{N}$ and

$$f(i + m_1 n_0), ..., f(i + m_s n_0) \in [k, k + n]$$

for $m_1 < m_2 < ...m_s, m_j \in \mathbb{N}, i + m_j n_0 \in A, j = 1, ..., s$. Then

$$f(i + m_s n_0) - f(i + m_1 n_0) \leq n.$$

From the other side, the inequality (1) implies

$$f(i + m_s n_0) - f(i + m_1 n_0) \geq \beta(m_s - m_1)n_0.$$

This yields $\beta(m_s - m_1)n_0 \leq n$ and so $m_s \leq m_1 + \frac{n}{\beta n_0}$. The numbers $i + m_j n_0, j = 1, ..., s$ belong to the interval $[r, r + \frac{n}{\beta}]$, where $r = i + m_1 n_0$. We get $s \leq A(r, r + \frac{n}{\beta})$, in the other words

$$E^{(i)}(k, k + n) \leq A\left(r, r + \frac{n}{\beta}\right), \tag{2}$$

thus $u(E^{(i)}) = 0$.   □

Let for $A \subset \mathbb{N}$, the symbol A_p, which has the same sense as on page 22. By the same procedure as the proof of Theorem 3 on page 20, we obtain:

Theorem 4. Let P be such set of primes that $\sum_P p^{-1} = \infty$. Then for $A \subset \mathbb{N}$ it holds

$$(\forall p \in P; u(A_p) = 0) \Rightarrow u(A) = 0. \tag{3}$$

In the paper [BF], thanks to similar ideas, using the Falting's result [Fa], it has been proven that the set of all exponents, which do not satisfy the Fermat last theorem, have the uniform density 0.

From Theorem 4, it can be derived that, for example, the sets $\{n^k; n \in \mathbb{N}\}, k = 1, 2, ...$ or $\{n!; n \in \mathbb{N}\}$ have the uniform density 0.

Lemma 2. Let P be such st of primes that $\sum_P p^{-1} = \infty$. Denote for $r = 1, 2, ...$ by $\mathbb{N}(r)$ the set of all positive integers which have at most r distinct prime divisors from P. Then $u(\mathbb{N}(r)) = 0, r = 1, 2, ...$

Proof: By induction with respect to r. Clearly $\mathbb{N}(0)_p = \emptyset$, for $p \in P$, thus (3) yields $u(\mathbb{N}(0)) = 0$.

It is easy to see that $\mathbb{N}(r + 1)_p \subset p\mathbb{N}(r)$, thus from (3) we obtain $u(\mathbb{N}(r)) = 0 \Rightarrow u(\mathbb{N}(r + 1)) = 0, r = 1, 2, ...$ □

Theorem 5. Let $f : \mathbb{N} \to \mathbb{N}$ be an arithmetic function, fulfilling the condition (a) from Lemma 1. Let P be such set of primes that $\sum_P p^{-1} = \infty$. Denote by $\omega(n)$ the number of distinct prime divisors from P of $n, n \in \mathbb{N}$. Let f fulfill moreover the condition
(b) There exists $a \in \mathbb{N}, a > 1$ that $a^{g(\omega(n))}|f(n)$ for $n \in \mathbb{N}$. Where $g : \mathbb{N} \to \mathbb{N}$ is such a function that $g(n) \to \infty$ for $n \to \infty$.
Then $u(F) = 0$, where $F = \{f(n), n \in \mathbb{N}\}$.

Proof: Let $s \in \mathbb{N}$. The set F can be decomposed to $F = F_1 \cup F_2$, where $F_1 = \{f(j); j \in \mathbb{N}, a^s | f(j)\}$ and $F_2 = F \setminus F_1$. Clearly $\bar{u}(F_1) \leq a^{-s}$. We prove $u(F_2) = 0$. The condition (b) yields that there exists r-nonnegative integer that $F_2 \subset f(\mathbb{N}(r))$, where $\mathbb{N}(r)$ is the set from Lemma 2. Thus Lemma 1 implies $u(F_2) = 0$. Therefore $\bar{u}(F) \leq a^{-s}$ and for $s \to \infty$ we obtain $u(F) = 0$.   □

Ideal convergence

Put
$$I_u = \{A \subset \mathbb{N}; u(A) = 0\}.$$

Clearly I_u is an admissible ideal (see page 26). Now we give an example that I_u does not satisfy the property (b) from Proposition 2, page 27.

Consider the arbitrary infinite set $A \in I_u$. Denote $B_k = A + k, k = 0, 1, \dots$. Clearly $B_k = I_u, k = 0, 1, \dots$. For each $s \in \mathbb{N}$, we have $\cup_{k=1}^{s} B_k = \cup_{n=1}^{\infty} \{a_n + 1, \dots, a_n + s\}$ where $A = \{a_n, n = 1, 2, \dots\}$. If $B_k \prec B$ for some $B \subset \mathbb{N}$, then for $s \in \mathbb{N}$ there exists $L \in \mathbb{N}$ that $\cup_{k=1}^{s} B_k \cap < L, \infty) \subset B$, therefore B contains a block of s consecutive integers. And so from i) page 67 we get $\overline{u}(B) = 1$, thus $B \notin I_u$. Proposition 2, page 27 yields that in this case I_u-convergence and I_u^*-convergence are not equivalent.

Well distribution

Analogical notion of uniform distribution is for the case of uniform density the well distribution. Let $\{x_n\}$ be a sequence of elements of the interval $< 0, 1)$. We say that this sequence is *well distributed* if and only if for every $x \in < 0, 1)$ the set $A(< 0, x), \{x_n\})$ (see page 32) belongs to $\mathcal{U}$ and $u(A(< 0, x), \{x_n\})) = x$ (see [KN], [DT], [SP]).

Using Theorem 3, we can derive Weyl's criterion, analogously to uniform distribution (see page 31):

If $\{x_n\}$ is a sequence of elements of the interval $< 0, 1)$, then it is well distributed if and only if

$$\lim_{N \to \infty} \frac{1}{N} \sum_{n=k}^{k+N} f(x_n) = \int_0^1 f(x)dx$$

uniformly for $k = 1, 2, \dots$ for every function f continuous on the interval $< 0, 1 >$.

Or the trigonometric form: **A sequence $\{x_n\}$ of elements of the interval $< 0, 1)$ is well distributed if and only if**

$$\lim_{N \to \infty} \frac{1}{N} \sum_{n=k}^{k+N} e^{2\pi i h x_n} = 0$$

uniformly for $k = 1, 2, \dots$ for every h integer, $h \neq 0$.

Sets of positive integers as increasing sequences

In the paper [GLS], it is proven, an analogical characterization of uniform density as Theorem 1 on page 9, for asymptotic density. We give the original proof.

Theorem 6. Let $A = \{a_1 < a_2 < \cdots < a_n < \cdots\} \subseteq N$ be an infinite set. Then $u(A) = L$ if and only if

$$\lim_{p \to \infty} \frac{p}{a_{k+p} - a_{k+1}} = L \qquad (a)$$

uniformly with respect to $k \geq 0$.

Proof: Let $u(A) = L$. Consider that for $p \geq 2$

$$\frac{p}{a_{k+p} - a_{k+1}} = \frac{A(a_{k+1}, a_{k+p})}{a_{k+p} - a_{k+1}}.$$

By Theorem 2 the right-hand side converges by $p \to \infty$ (uniformly with respect to $k \geq 0$) $u(A) = L$. Hence (a) holds.

2. Suppose that (a) holds (uniformly with respect to $k \geq 0$). By Theorem 1.1 it suffices to prove that

$$\lim_{p \to \infty} \frac{A(t+1, t+p)}{p} = L$$

uniformly with respect to $t \geq 0$.

We shall show it. Suppose in the first place that $t \geq a_1$. Then there exist $k, s \in N$ such that

$$a_k < t+1 \leq a_{k+1} < \cdots < a_{k+s} \leq t+p < a_{k+s+1}.$$

Then $A(t+1, t+p)$ equals s and so

$$\frac{A(t+1, t+p)}{p} = \frac{s}{p}.$$

Further, on the basis of the choice of numbers k, s, we get

$$a_{k+s} - a_{k+1} \leq p - 1 < a_{k+s+1} - a_k.$$

Therefore

$$\frac{s}{a_{k+s+1} - a_k + 1} < \frac{A(t+1, t+p)}{p} < \frac{s}{a_{k+s} - a_{k+1}}. \tag{0}$$

But $-a_k + 1 \leq -a_{k-1}$, so that

$$\frac{s}{a_{k+s+1} - a_k + 1} \geq \frac{s}{a_{k+s+1} - a_{k-1}} =$$

$$= \frac{s+3}{a_{k+s+1} - a_{k-1}} \frac{s}{s+3} =$$

$$= \frac{s+3}{a_{k+s+1} - a_k - 1} \left(1 - \frac{3}{s+3}\right).$$

So we get in whole

$$\frac{s+3}{a_{k+s+1} - a_{k-1}} \left(1 - \frac{3}{s+3}\right) < \frac{A(t+1, t+p)}{p} < \frac{s}{a_{k+s} - a_{k+1}}. \tag{1}$$

Let $\gamma > 0$. Then by assumption (see(a)) there exists a v_0 such that for each $v > v_0$ we have

$$-\gamma < \frac{v}{a_{k+v} - a_{k+1}} - L < \gamma \tag{2}$$

for all $k \geq 0$.

Using (0) we get from (1)

$$\frac{s+3}{a_{k+s+1}-a_{k-1}}-L-\frac{3}{a_{k+s+1}-a_{k-1}}<\frac{A(t+1,t+p)}{p}-L<\frac{s}{a_{k+s}-a_{k+1}}-L.$$

Let $s>v_0$. Then by (2) the right-hand side is less than γ. On the left-hand sidem,we get

$$\frac{s+3}{a_{k+s+1}-a_{k-1}}-L>-\gamma.$$

Further

$$\frac{-3}{a_{k+s+1}-a_{k-1}}\geq\frac{-3}{s+2},$$

since

$$a_{k+s+1}-a_{k-1}=(a_k-a_{k-1})+(a_{k+1}-a_k)+\cdots+(a_{k+s+1}-a_{k+s})$$

and each summand on the right-hand side is ≥ 1.

Hence for every $t\geq a_1$,we get from (5) $(s>v_0)$

$$-\gamma-\frac{3}{s+2}<\frac{A(t+1,t+p)}{p}-L<\gamma. \qquad (3)$$

From this

$$\lim_{p\to\infty}\frac{A(t+1,t+p)}{p}=L$$

uniformly with respect to $t\geq a_1$.

It remains the case if $0\leq t<a_1$. Since there is only a finite number of such t's, it suffices to show that for each fixed t, $0\leq t\leq a_1$ we have

$$\lim_{p\to\infty}\frac{A(t+1,t+p)}{p}=L \qquad (4)$$

If t is fixed, $0\leq t<a_1$ and p is sufficiently large, we can determine a k such that $a_k\leq t+p<a_{k+1}$. Then

$$0\leq t<a_1<a_2<\cdots<a_k\leq t+p<a_{k+1}$$

and

$$A(t+1,t+p)=A(t+1,a_1)+A(a_2,a_k). \qquad (5)$$

From this

$$p<a_{k+1},\quad p>a_k-a_1 \qquad (6)$$

and so from (5), (6) we obtain

$$\frac{A(t+1,a_1)}{p}+\frac{A(a_2,a_{k+1})-1}{p}\leq\frac{A(t+1,t+p)}{p}\leq\frac{A(t+1,a_1)}{p}+\frac{k-1}{a_k-a_1}. \qquad (7)$$

Obviously, we have $A(t+1, a_1) \le a_1$ and so

$$\frac{A(t+1, a_1)}{p} = o(1) \qquad (p \to \infty).$$

We arrange the left-hand side of (7). We get

$$\frac{A(a_2, a_{k+1}) - 1}{a_{k+1}} = -\frac{1}{a_{k+1}} + \frac{k}{a_{k+1} - a_2} \frac{a_{k+1} - a_2}{a_{k+1}} = o(1) + \frac{k}{a_{k+1} - a_2}$$

(if $p \to \infty$ then $k \to \infty$, as well).

In whole we have

$$\frac{k}{a_{k+1} - a_2} + o(1) \le \frac{A(t+1, t+p)}{p} \le \frac{k-1}{a_k - a_1} + o(1).$$

If $p \to \infty$, then $k \to \infty$ and by assumption (cf. (2)) the terms

$$\frac{k-1}{a_k - a_1} - L, \qquad \frac{k}{a_{k+1} - a_2} - L$$

converge to zero. But then (7) yields

$$\lim_{p \to \infty} \frac{A(t+1, t+p)}{p} = L$$

uniformly with respect to $t \ge 0$. So $u(A) = L$. $\qquad \square$

Corollary. Let $A = \{a_1 < a_2 < \cdots\} \subseteq N$ be a lacunary set, i.e.

$$\lim_{n \to \infty} (a_{n+1} - a_n) = +\infty.$$

Then $u(A) = 0.$

Proof: Let $\varepsilon > 0$. Choose $M \in N$ such that $M^{-1} < \varepsilon$. By the assumption that there exists an n_0 such that for each $n > n_0$ we get $a_{n+1} - a_n > M$.

Let $k > n_0$, $s \in N$, $s > 1$. Then

$$a_{k+s} - a_{k+1} = (a_{k+2} - a_{k+1}) + (a_{k+3} - a_{k+2}) + \cdots \cdots + (a_{k+s} - a_{k+s-1}) > (s-1)M$$

and so

$$\frac{s}{a_{k+s} - a_{k+1}} < \frac{s}{(s-1)M} < 2\varepsilon.$$

Hence for each $k > n_0$ and $s \ge 2$ we have

$$\frac{s}{a_{k+s} - a_{k+1}} < 2\varepsilon.$$

If $0 \le k \le n_0$, k is fixed, then

$$\lim_{s \to \infty} \frac{s}{a_{k+s} - a_{k+1}} = 0, \tag{8}$$

since, for sufficiently large s

$$a_{k+s} - a_{k+1} = [(a_{k+2} - a_{k+1}) + \cdots + (a_{n_0+1} - a_{n_0})]+$$

$$+[(a_{n_0+2} - a_{n_0+1}) + \cdots + (a_{k+s} - a_{k+s-1})] >$$

$$> M(k + s - n_0 - 1) \geq M(s - (n_0 + 1)). \tag{9}$$

There exists only a finite number of k's with $0 \leq k \leq n_0$, so we see that (9) holds uniformly with respect to k. So we in whole

$$\lim_{s \to \infty} \frac{s}{a_{k+s} - a_{k+1}} = 0$$

uniformly with respect to $k \geq 0$. So according to Theorem 6, we have $u(A) = 0$. $\qquad \square$

Remark. The assumption in Theorem cannot be replaced by the weaker assumption

$$\lim_{n \to \infty} \overline{\lim}(a_{n+1} - a_n) = +\infty \tag{10}$$

This can be shown by the following example:

$$A = \bigcup_{k=1}^{\infty} \{k! + 1, k! + 2, \ldots, k! + k\} = \{a_1 < a_2 < \cdots < a_n < \cdots\}.$$

Here we have $\underline{u}(A) = 0$, $\overline{u}(A) = 1$ and (10) is satisfied.

Example. Let $\alpha \in R$, $\alpha > 1$. Put $a_k = [k\alpha]$, $(k = 1, 2, \ldots)$, where $[v]$ denotes the integer part of v. We show that the uniform density of the set A is $\frac{1}{\alpha}$. This follows from Theorem 6, since

$$\lim_{p \to \infty} \frac{p}{a_{k+p} - a_{k+1}} = \frac{1}{\alpha}$$

uniformly with respect to $k \geq 0$. This uniform convergence can be shown by a simple calculation which gives the estimates ($p \geq 2$)

$$\frac{p}{(p-1)\alpha + 1} \leq \frac{p}{a_{k+p} - a_{k+1}} \leq \frac{p}{(p-1)\alpha - 1}.$$

Theorem 6 we can now apply for investigation of transformed sets:

Theorem 7. Let $g : \mathbb{N} \to \mathbb{N}$ be an injection fulfilling the condition

$$\lim_{n \to \infty} \frac{g(n + k) - g(k)}{n} = 1 \tag{1}$$

uniformly for $k = 1, 2, \cdots$. Then for every $A \in \mathcal{U}$ there holds $g(A) \in \mathcal{U}$ and $u(g(A)) = u(A)$.

Proof: The condition (1) yields that for two sequences $\{h_1(n, k)\}$, $\{h_2(n, k)\}$ such that $h_1(n, k) - h_2(n, k) \to \infty$, $n \to \infty$ uniformly for $k = 1, 2, \cdots$ we have

$$\frac{g(h_1(n, k)) - g(h_2(n, k))}{h_1(n, k) - h_2(n, k)} \rightrightarrows 1, \quad n \to \infty \tag{2}$$

(As usual, we use the symbol $\rightrightarrows$ for the uniform convergence.)

Let $A = \{a(1) < a(2) < \ldots\}$ be an infinite set, which has the uniform density and $u(A) = \alpha$.

From Theorem 6 we obtain

$$\frac{n}{a(n+k) - a(k)} \rightrightarrows \alpha, \quad n \to \infty \tag{3}$$

Put $g(A) = \{g(a(1)), g(a(2)), \ldots\}$. These elements are not necessarily arranged to their magnitude. Clearly $a(n+k) - a(k) \geq n$, and so $a(n+k) - a(k) \rightrightarrows \infty$ as $n \to \infty$. The relation (2) now implies

$$\frac{g(a(n+k)) - g(a(k))}{a(n+k) - a(k)} \rightrightarrows 1, \quad n \to \infty \tag{4}$$

Therefore for a suitable n_o, the fraction on the left side is positive for $k = 1, 2, \cdots$, thus $g(a(n_0 + k)) > g(a(k))$, $k = 1, 2, \cdots$. And so we see that in the set $g(A)$, we can decompose into a union of disjoint sets

$$g(A) = B_1 \cup B_2 \cup \cdots \cup B_{n_0} \tag{5}$$

where

$$B_j = \{g(a(j)) < g(a(j + n_0)) < \cdots g(a(j + rn_0)) \cdots\} \, j = 1, \cdots, n_0.$$

The relation (3) now implies

$$\frac{r \cdot n_0}{a(j + (r+k)n_0) - a(j + k \cdot n_0)} \rightrightarrows \alpha, \quad r \to \infty \tag{6}$$

Moreover the relation (2) yields

$$\frac{g(a(j + (k+r)n_0)) - g(a(j + k \cdot n_0))}{a(j + (k+r)n_0) - a(j + k \cdot n_0)} \rightrightarrows 1, \quad r \to \infty \tag{7}$$

because the denominator is $\geq r \cdot n_0$ and so tends to ∞ uniformly for $k = 1, 2, \cdots$.

Thus from (6) and (7) we can deduce

$$\frac{r}{g(a(j + (k+r)n_0)) - g(a(j + k \cdot n_o))} \rightrightarrows \frac{\alpha}{n_0}, \quad r \to \infty$$

and so $u(B_j) = \frac{\alpha}{n_0}$, $j = 1, \cdots, n_0$. From (5) we have $u(g(A)) = \alpha$. $\qquad \square$

Consider $g(n) = n + c \cdot \log n + O(1)$. Then $g(n+k) - g(k) = n + c \cdot \log\left(\frac{n}{k} + 1\right) + O(1)$, but $O \leq \log\left(\frac{n}{k} + 1\right) \leq \log(n+1)$ and g fulfills (1). Analogously it can be proven that for $r_1, r_2, \cdots, r_j > 1$ the functions

$$g(n) = n + c_1 \log_{r_1}^n + c_2 \log_{r_2}^{(n)} + \cdots + O(1)$$

fulfills (1).

Darboux property of uniform density

The idea of proof of Corollary 1, page 9, can be by Theorem 6 used for the uniform density:

Theorem 8. The uniform density has the Darboux property.

Proof: Let $u(A) = \delta > 0$,

$$A = \{a_1 < a_2 < \cdots < a_k < \cdots\}$$

and $0 < t < \delta$. Construct the set

$$B = \{b_1 < b_2 < \cdots < b_k < \cdots\}$$

in such a way that we set

$$b_k = a_{[k\frac{\delta}{t}]} \qquad (k = 1, 2, \ldots).$$

Put $n_k = [k\frac{\delta}{t}]$ $(k = 1, 2, \ldots)$. Then $n_1 < n_2 < \cdots < n_k < \cdots < n_k < \cdots$,

$$B = \{a_{n_1} < a_{n_2} < \cdots < a_{n_k} < \cdots\}, \qquad B \subseteq A.$$

We prove that $u(B) = t$.

By Theorem 6, it suffices to show that

$$\lim_{p \to \infty} \frac{p}{b_{m+p} - b_{m+1}} = t \tag{1}$$

uniformly with respect to $m \geq 0$.

We have $(p > 1)$

$$\frac{p}{b_{m+p} - b_{m+1}} = \frac{p}{a_{n_{m+p}} - a_{n_{m+1}}}.$$

By a simple arrangement we get

$$\frac{p}{b_{m+p} - b_{m+1}} = \frac{n_{m+p} - n_{m+1} + 1}{a_{n_{m+p}} - a_{n_{m+1}}} \frac{p}{n_{m+p} - n_{m+1} + 1}. \tag{2}$$

A simple estimation gives

$$(p-1)\frac{\delta}{t} - 1 < n_{m+p} - n_{m+1} < (p-1)\frac{\delta}{t} + 1.$$

Using this in (2) we get

$$\lim_{p \to \infty} \frac{p}{n_{m+p} - n_{m+1} + 1} = \frac{t}{\delta} \tag{3}$$

uniformly with respect to $m \geq 0$.

Furthermore, by assumption

$$\lim_{p \to \infty} \frac{p}{a_{s+p} - a_{s+1}} = \delta$$

uniformly with respect to $s \geq 0$ (Theorem 6).

So we get

$$\lim_{p \to \infty} \frac{n_{m+p} - n_{m+1} + 1}{a_{n_{m+p}} - a_{n_{m+1}}} = \delta \tag{4}$$

uniformly with respect to $m \geq 0$ since the sequence

$$\left(\frac{n_{m+p} - n_{m+1} + 1}{a_{n_{m+p}} - a_{n_{m+1}}} \right)_{p=2}^{\infty}$$

is a subsequence of the sequence

$$\left(\frac{p}{a_{s+p} - a_{s+1}} \right)_{p=1}^{\infty}.$$

By (2), (3), (4), we get (1) uniformly with respect to $m \geq 0$. $\square$

Some Remarks On Weight Density

The concept of weight density is the generalization of asymptotic density analogical to the Stjelties measure. The properties of this type of density are studied in several papers. We start with the definition:

Suppose that $\{c_j\}$ is the sequence of positive real numbers such that $\sum_{j=1}^{\infty} c_j = \infty$. This sequence will be called the sequence of weights. Let $A \subset \mathbb{N}$. Put

$$S(A, N) = \sum_{\substack{j \leq N \\ j \in A}} c_j, \quad S(N) = \sum_{j \leq N} c_j.$$

If there exists

$$\lim_{N \to \infty} \frac{S(A, N)}{S(N)},$$

then we say that the set A has weighed asymptotic density and will denote as $d_c(A)$.

Analogously, as in the case of asymptotic density, we can define the *upper weight density* of the set A as

$$\overline{d}_c(A) = \limsup_{N \to \infty} \frac{S(A, N)}{S(N)}$$

and *lower asymptotic density* of A as

$$\underline{d}_c(A) = \liminf_{N \to \infty} \frac{S(A, N)}{S(N)}.$$

By D_c we will denote the set of all sets, which has the weighted asymptotic density.

Remark: In a special case, if $c_j = 1$ for all j, then the weighted asymptotic density is just asymptotic density and is denoted by $d(A)$. For $c_n = \frac{1}{n}, n = 1, 2, ...$ the corresponding weight density is well known as *logarithmic density*. It is proven that every set which has asymptotic density has logarithmic density also.

Theorem 1. Let $c = (c_n), c_n > 0, \sum_{n=1}^{\infty} c_n = +\infty$. **Put**

$$\mathcal{I}_c = \left\{ A \subseteq \mathbb{N} : d_c(A) = 0 \right\}.$$

Then $\mathcal{I}_c$ is an admissible ideal and $\mathcal{I}_c$ satisfies has the property (b) from Proposition 2 on the page 27.

Proof: The fact that $\mathcal{I}_c$ is admissible follows immediately from the condition $\sum_{n=1}^{\infty} c_n = +\infty$. Let $B_1, B_2, \cdots \subseteq \mathbb{N}$ and $d_c(B_k) = 0, k = 1, 2, ...$ Put $D_k = B_1 \cup B_2 \cdots \cup B_k$, $k = 1, 2, ...$ Then $D_1 \subset D_2 \subset \cdots \subset D_k \subset ...$ Let $S(N)$ and $S(A, N)$ have the same sense as in the introduction. Clearly $d_c(D_k) = 0, k = 1, 2, ...$ and so there exists a sequence of indices $N_1 < N_2 < \cdots < N_k < ...$ such that

$$\frac{S(D_k, N)}{S(N)} < \frac{1}{k+1}, \qquad N \geqslant N_k, \ k = 1, 2, ... \tag{1}$$

Put $D'_k = D_k \setminus \{a \in D_k : a \leqslant N_k\}$ and $B = \bigcup_{k=1}^{\infty} D'_k$. Then $B_k \subset D'_k \prec D_k \subset B$. Thus $B_k \prec B$, $k = 1, 2, \ldots$ Let $N > N_k$. Thus $N_j < N \leqslant N_{j+1}$ for some $j \geqslant k$. Thus if $n \leq N$, then $n \notin D'_h$ for $h \geqslant j+1$ and so if $n \leqslant N$ and $n \in B$, then $n \in D'_l$ for some $l \leqslant j$. From the monotonicity of $\{D_r\}$ we have now

$$n \in B \wedge n \leqslant N \implies n \in D_j .$$

This yields $S(B, N) \leqslant S(D_j, N)$. Therefore

$$\frac{S(B, N)}{S(N)} \leqslant \frac{S(D_j, N)}{S(N)} .$$

But $N \geqslant N_j$ and so from (1) we obtain

$$\frac{S(B, N)}{S(N)} \leqslant \frac{1}{j+1} \leqslant \frac{1}{k+1} .$$

This implies $d_c(B) = 0$. $\qquad\qquad\qquad\qquad\qquad\qquad\qquad\qquad\qquad\qquad\qquad\square$

Thus, in this case also, there holds that I_c convergence and I_c^* convergence are equivalent, (see Proposition 2, page 27).

In the paper [MMST], the following observations are made:
Put for $A \subset \mathbb{N}, N \in \mathbb{N}$

$$d_N(A) = \frac{S(A, N)}{S(N)} .$$

Then by an easy calculation, we get

$$d_N(A) - d_{N-1}(A) = (\chi_A(N) - d_{N-1}(A)) \frac{c_N}{S(N)} .$$

Analyzing the first factor on the right-hand side of the last equality we get
Theorem 2.

a) **If there exists $A \in \mathcal{D}_c$ such that $0 < d_c(A) < 1$, then**

$$\lim_{N \to \infty} \frac{c_N}{S(N)} = 0. \qquad\qquad\qquad\qquad (*)$$

b) **If $(*)$ holds, then for every $A \subset \mathbb{N}$ we have $\lim_{N \to \infty} d_N(A) - d_{N-1}(A) = 0$.**

Thus we see that if $\limsup_{N \to \infty} \frac{c_N}{S(N)} > 0$ then the range of the set function d_C on $\mathcal{D}_C$ contains only 0 and 1. This leads to the question of the Darboux property of weight density, solved also in [MMST]. The following result is proved:

Theorem 3. Let $c = (c_n), c_n > 0, \sum_{n=1}^{\infty} c_n = +\infty$. Then d_c has the Darboux property on $\mathcal{D}_c$ if and only if $(*)$ holds.

Proof: The necessity of $(*)$ follows immediately from part a) of the previous theorem. For he proof of sufficiency, we start with following lemma:

Lemma. Let $(*)$ holds, then for every $v \in\, <0, 1>$ there exists $B \in \mathcal{D}_c$ that $d_c(B) = v$.

Proof: The cases $v = 0$ and $v = 1$ are trivial. Suppose $v \in (0, 1)$. We shall construct the set B in the form $B = \cup_{n=1}^{\infty} \mathbb{N} \cap (a_n, b_n >$ in the following way: Assume that we have the intervals $(a_1, b_1 >, ..., (a_n, b_n >$ such that $d_{b_n}(B) > v$. Then we choose the interval $(a_{n+1}, b_{n+1} >$ in the order that

$$d_{a_{n+1}}(B) < v \leq d_{a_{n+1}-1}(B)$$

$$d_{b_{n+1}-1}(B) < v < d_{b_{n+1}}(B).$$

Thus from Theorem 2, we get $\lim_{n \to \infty} d_{a_n}(B) = v = \lim_{n \to \infty} d_{b_n}(B)$. From the monotonicity of the sequence $d_N(B)$ on the intervals $< a_n, b_n >$ and $< b_n + 1, a_{n+1} - 1 >$ we get $\lim_{N \to \infty} d_N(B) = v$. $\qquad \square$

Now we can continue with the proof of Theorem 3. Let $A \in \mathcal{D}_c$ and $a \in < 0, d_c(A) >$. The case $d_c(A) = 0$ is trivial, thus suppose that $d_c(A) > 0$. Let $A = \{a_1 < a_2 < ...\}$. Put $c'_n = c_{a_n}, n = 1, 2, ...$ Then the sequence $c' = \{c'_n\}$ satisfies the condition $(*)$ also. The previous Lemma provides here the existence of suitable set $I \in \mathcal{D}_{c'}$ that $d_{c'}(I) = \frac{a}{d_c(A)}$. Put $B = \{a_k; k \in I\}$. Then

$$d_N(B) = \frac{\sum_{a_k \leq N, k \in I} c_{a_k}}{S(N)} =$$

$$= \frac{S(N)}{\sum_{a_k \leq N} c_{a_k}} \cdot \frac{\sum_{a_k \leq N, k \in I} c_{a_k}}{\sum_{a_k \leq N} c_{a_k}}.$$

And so

$$\lim_{N \to \infty} d_N(B) = d_c(A) d_{c'}(B) = a.$$

$\qquad \square$

Arithmetic progressions

If we consider the sequence on weights $\{c_n\}$ where $c_{2n} = 1, c_{2n+1} = 2$ then $d_c((2)) = \frac{1}{3}, d_c(1 + (2)) = \frac{2}{3}$. In the following theorem we give a condition which excludes similar cases.

Theorem 4. Let the sequence $c = \{c_n\}$ satisfies the condition

$$\lim_{n \to \infty} \frac{c_{n+1}}{c_n} = 1. \tag{2}$$

Then

(a) **for every $A \subseteq \mathbb{N}$ having the weight density d_c we have $d_c(A + 1) = d_c(A)$.**

(b) **For $m \in \mathbb{N}, r = 0, 1, 2, \ldots$ we have $d_c(r + (m)) = \frac{1}{m}$.**

Proof.

(a) If $\sum_{k \in A} c_k < \infty$, then (2) yields $\sum_{k \in A} c_{k+1} < \infty$ and $d_c(A) = 0 = d_c(A + 1)$. Suppose $\sum_{k \in A} c_k = \infty$. Let $A = \{k_1 < k_2 < \ldots\}$ Then $S(A + 1, n) = \sum_{k_j + 1 \leq n} c_{k_j + 1} =$

$\sum_{k_j \leqslant n-1} c_{k_j+1}$. Thus from (2) and the Stolz theorem we have $\frac{S(A+1,n)}{S(A,n-1)} \to 1$ as $n \to \infty$. Clearly

$$\frac{S(A+1,n)}{S(n)} = \frac{S(A,n-1)}{S(n-1)} \cdot \frac{S(n-1)}{S(n)} \cdot \frac{S(A+1,n)}{S(A,n-1)}.$$

It can be verified easily that $\frac{S(n-1)}{S(n)} \to 1$, $n \to \infty$. Thus, from the last equality, we obtain the assertion. (b)

(b) Using (a) it suffices to prove that $d_c((m)) = \frac{1}{m}$. From (2) we have that for each $k \in \mathbb{N}$ it holds

$$\lim_{n\to\infty} \frac{c_{n+k}}{c_n} = 1. \tag{4}$$

Denote $y_j = c_{(j-1)\cdot m+1} + \cdots + c_{j\cdot m}$, $j = 1, 2, \ldots$ The term y_j has m summands and so from (4) we obtain

$$\lim_{n\to\infty} \frac{c_{j\cdot m}}{y_j} = \frac{1}{m}. \tag{5}$$

Clearly $S(j \cdot m) = y_1 + \cdots + y_j$ and $S((m), j \cdot m) = c_m + \cdots + c_{j\cdot m}$. Thus from (5) and Stolz's Theorem we have

$$\lim_{n\to\infty} \frac{S((m), j \cdot m)}{S(j \cdot m)} = \frac{1}{m}. \tag{6}$$

Arbitrary $n \in \mathbb{N}$ can be expressed in the form $n = m \cdot j_n + k_n$, where $j_n \to \infty$ as $n \to \infty$ and $k_n < m$. Then we have

$$S(n) - S(m \cdot j_n) \leqslant c_n + \cdots + c_{n-m} \tag{7}$$

and

$$S((m), n) - S((m), m \cdot j_n) \leqslant c_n + \cdots + c_{n-m}. \tag{8}$$

The condition (2) guarantees that

$$\lim_{n\to\infty} \frac{c_{n-k}}{c_1 + \cdots + c_n} = 0$$

is fulfilled for arbitrary k. Thus (7) yields

$$\lim_{n\to\infty} \frac{S(m \cdot j_n)}{S(n)} = 1. \tag{9}$$

From (8), we have

$$\lim_{n\to\infty} \frac{S((m), n) - S((m), m \cdot j_n)}{S(n)} = 0$$

and the assertion follows from (6) and (9).

Permutations preserving weight density

In the paper [OB], the author characterizes the set of permutations of $\mathbb{N}$, which preserve the asymptotic density as the permutations g having the property:

$$\lim_{N \to \infty} \frac{1}{N} \mid \{1 \le j \le N; g(j) > N\} \mid = 0.$$

This set forms a subgroup of the group $\mathbb{N}$ with respect to composition and is called the Lévy group, we recall this notion from page 19.

In the case of weighted asymptotic density, the condition $\lim_{N \to \infty} \frac{1}{N} \mid \{1 \le j \le N; g(j) > N\} \mid = 0$ splits into two conditions:

$$\lim_{N \to \infty} \frac{1}{S(N)} \sum_{\substack{j \le N \\ g(j) > N}} c_j = 0 \tag{7}$$

$$\lim_{N \to \infty} \frac{1}{S(N)} \sum_{\substack{j > N \\ g(j) \le N}} c_{g(j)} = 0, \tag{8}$$

but it is not sufficient for preserving the weighted asymptotic density, as the next example shows.

Example. Let the weights be such that $c_{2k} = 1$, $c_{2k+1} = 0.5$ and let g be such permutation that $g(2k-1) = 2k$ and $g(2k) = 2k-1$. Then $\sum_{\substack{j \le N \\ g(j) > N}} c_j \le 0.5$, because just for one element $j \le N$ the $g(j)$ can exceed the number N, so $\lim_{N \to \infty} \frac{1}{S(N)} \sum_{\substack{j \le N \\ g(j) > N}} c_j = 0$. Analogously $\lim_{N \to \infty} \frac{1}{S(N)} \sum_{\substack{j > N \\ g(j) \le N}} c_{g(j)} = 0$. But this permutation does not preserve the weighted asymptotic density, because for the set of even number A_{2k} we have $d_c(A_{2k}) = \frac{2}{3}$ and the image is the set of odd number $g(A_{2k}) = A_{2k+1}$ and $d_c(g(A_{2k})) = d_c(A_{2k+1}) = \frac{1}{3} \ne d_c(A_{2k})$.

We recall the statement well known as **Stolz Theorem**: Let α_n, β_n be two sequences of positive real numbers, and $\sum \beta_n = \infty$. Then

$$\lim_{n \to \infty} \frac{\alpha_n}{\beta_n} = L \Rightarrow \lim_{N \to \infty} \frac{\sum_{n \le N} \alpha_n}{\sum_{n \le N} \beta_n} = L.$$

Let G_c be the set of all permutations g which satisfy the condition (7) and (8) and

$$\lim_{j \to \infty} \frac{c_{g(j)}}{c_j} = 1. \tag{9}$$

Lemma. G_c is a group with respect to the composition of permutations.

Proof: Clearly the identical belongs to G_c, and the set of permutations fulfilling condition (9) satisfies the conditions of the group. Let $f, g \in G_c$. Thus

$$\lim_{N \to \infty} \frac{1}{S(N)} \sum_{\substack{j \le N \\ f(j) > N}} c_j = 0 = \lim_{N \to \infty} \frac{1}{S(N)} \sum_{\substack{j > N \\ f(j) \le N}} c_{f(j)}$$

$$\lim_{N\to\infty} \frac{1}{S(N)} \sum_{\substack{j\le N \\ g(j)>N}} c_j = 0 = \lim_{N\to\infty} \frac{1}{S(N)} \sum_{\substack{j>N \\ g(j)\le N}} c_{g(j)}$$

We prove that $f \circ g$ satisfies (7), (8). There holds

$$\lim_{N\to\infty} \frac{1}{S(N)} \sum_{\substack{j\le N \\ (f\circ g)(j)>N}} c_j = \lim_{N\to\infty} \frac{1}{S(N)} \sum_{\substack{j\le N \\ g(f(j))>N}} c_j =$$

$$= \lim_{N\to\infty} \frac{1}{S(N)} \Big(\sum_{\substack{j\le N \\ g(f(j))>N \\ f(j)\le N}} c_j + \sum_{\substack{j\le N \\ g(f(j))>N \\ f(j)>N}} c_j \Big) \le$$

$$\le \lim_{N\to\infty} \frac{1}{S(N)} \Big(\sum_{\substack{f(j)\le N \\ g(f(j))>N}} c_j + \sum_{\substack{j\le N \\ f(j)>N}} c_j \Big) = \lim_{N\to\infty} \frac{1}{S(N)} \sum_{\substack{f(j)\le N \\ g(f(j))>N}} c_j$$

because $f \in G_c$. If the sum $\displaystyle\sum_{\substack{N=1 \\ f(j)\le N \\ g(f(j))>N}}^{\infty} c_j < \infty$, then $\displaystyle\lim_{N\to\infty} \frac{1}{S(N)} \sum_{\substack{f(j)\le N \\ g(f(j))>N}} c_j = 0$. If the sum

$\displaystyle\sum_{\substack{N=1 \\ f(j)\le N \\ g(f(j))>N}}^{\infty} c_j = \infty$, then because $\displaystyle\lim_{j\to\infty} \frac{c_{f(j)}}{c_j} = 1$, using the Stoltz theorem we have

$$\lim_{N\to\infty} \frac{\displaystyle\sum_{\substack{f(j)\le N \\ g(f(j))>N}} c_{f(j)}}{\displaystyle\sum_{\substack{f(j)\le N \\ g(f(j))>N}} c_j} = 1,$$

and so

$$\lim_{N\to\infty} \frac{1}{S(N)} \sum_{\substack{f(j)\le N \\ g(f(j))>N}} c_j = \lim_{N\to\infty} \frac{1}{S(N)} \sum_{\substack{f(j)\le N \\ g(f(j))>N}} c_{f(j)} = 0,$$

because $g \in G_c$. Analogously, the second limit is equal to zero.

Now we show that for every $f \in G_c$ we have $f^{-1} \in G_c$. Let $f \in G_c$, so

$$\lim_{N\to\infty} \frac{1}{S(N)} \sum_{\substack{j\le N \\ f(j)>N}} c_j = 0,$$

and

$$\lim_{N\to\infty} \frac{1}{S(N)} \sum_{\substack{j>N \\ f(j)\le N}} c_{f(j)} = 0$$

Using the $f(f^{-1}(j)) = j$ we have

$$\lim_{N \to \infty} \frac{1}{S(N)} \sum_{\substack{j \le N \\ f^{-1}(j) > N}} c_j = \lim_{N \to \infty} \frac{1}{S(N)} \sum_{\substack{f(f^{-1}(j)) \le N \\ f^{-1}(j) > N}} c_{f(f^{-1}(j))} = 0,$$

because $f \in G_c$. Analogously we prove the second limit.

Theorem 5. If $g \in G_c$, then for any set $S \subset \mathbb{N}$ such that $S \in D_c$, i.e. it has the weighted asymptotic density, the set $g(S) \in D_c$ and $d_c(g(S)) = d_c(S)$.

Proof: Let us denote by $F_N^+(g) = \{j \in \mathbb{N}, j \le N : g(j) > N\}$. For any set $S \subset \mathbb{N}$ and any permutation g we have

$$S \cap \{g(1), g(2), \dots, g(N)\} \subseteq F_N^+(g) \cup (S \cap \{1, 2, \dots, N\}).$$

Now let $g \in G_c$ and $S \subset \mathbb{N}, S \in D_c$. Then the upper weighted asymptotic density

$$\overline{d}_c(g^{-1}(S)) = \limsup_{N \to \infty} \frac{1}{S(N)} \sum_{\substack{j \le N \\ j \in g^{-1}(S)}} c_j =$$

$$= \limsup_{N \to \infty} \frac{1}{S(N)} \sum_{\substack{j \le N \\ g(j) \in S}} c_j \le \limsup_{N \to \infty} \frac{1}{S(N)} \Big(\sum_{\substack{j \le N \\ g(j) > N}} c_j + \sum_{\substack{i \le N \\ i \in S \\ i = g(j)}} c_j \Big) =$$

$$= \limsup_{N \to \infty} \frac{1}{S(N)} \Big(\sum_{\substack{j \le N \\ g(j) > N}} c_j + \sum_{\substack{i \le N \\ i \in S \\ i = g(j)}} c_{g^{-1}(i)} \Big) = \limsup_{N \to \infty} \frac{1}{S(N)} \sum_{\substack{i \le N \\ i \in S}} c_{g^{-1}(i)},$$

because $g \in G_c$.

If the sum

$$\sum_{\substack{N=1 \\ i \le N \\ i \in S}}^{\infty} c_{g^{-1}(i)} = \infty,$$

then because

$$\lim_{i \to \infty} \frac{c_i}{c_{g^{-1}(i)}} = 1,$$

using the Stoltz theorem, we have

$$\lim_{N \to \infty} \frac{\sum_{\substack{i \le N \\ i \in S}} c_i}{\sum_{\substack{i \le N \\ i \in S}} c_{g^{-1}(i)}} = 1,$$

and so it is equal to

$$= \limsup_{N \to \infty} \frac{1}{S(N)} \sum_{\substack{i \le N \\ i \in S}} c_i = \overline{d}_c(S).$$

So $\overline{d}_c(g^{-1}(S)) \leq \overline{d}_c(S)$. Using the fact, that G_c is a group, we have $g, g^{-1} \in G_c$, so we obtain reverse inequality

$$\overline{d}_c(S) = \overline{d}_c(g(g^{-1}(S))) \leq \overline{d}_c(g^{-1}(S)),$$

and so $\overline{d}_c(g^{-1}(S)) = \overline{d}_c(S)$. Similarly for the lower weighted asymptotic density we have $\underline{d}_c(g^{-1}(S)) = \underline{d}_c(S)$. So if the set $S \in D_c$ then the set $g(S) \in D_c$, and

$$\overline{d}_c(g^{-1}(S)) = \overline{d}_c(S) = \underline{d}_c(S) = \underline{d}_c(g^{-1}(S)),$$

i.e. $d_c(S) = d_c(g(S))$.

If the sum $\sum_{\substack{N=1 \\ i \leq N \\ i \in S}}^{\infty} c_{g^{-1}(i)} < \infty$, then $d_c(g^{-1}(S)) = 0$. In this case the sum $\sum_{\substack{N=1 \\ i \leq N \\ i \in \mathbb{N} \setminus S}}^{\infty} c_{g^{-1}(i)} = \infty$

by using the same way for the set $\mathbb{N} - S$ we obtain that

$$d_c(\mathbb{N} \setminus S) = d_c(g^{-1}(\mathbb{N} \setminus S)) = 1 - d_c(g^{-1}(S)) = 1 - 0 = 1$$

and because $d_c(\mathbb{N} \setminus S) = 1 - d_c(S)$ we have $d_c(S) = 0 = d_c(g^{-1}(S))$. $\qquad\square$

Remark 1. We can construct the weights such that every permutation will preserve the weighted asymptotic density for any set $S \in D_c$.

Lemma 1. Let the weights $\{c_n\}$ be such that

$$\lim_{N \to \infty} \frac{c_N}{\sum_{j=1}^{N} c_j} = 1.$$

Then for any $S \subset \mathbb{N}$ holds $S \in D_c$ if and only if S is finite or $\mathbb{N} - S$ is finite, and for any g. if $S \in D_c$, then $g(S) \in D_c$, and $d_c(S) = d_c(g(S))$.

Proof: Let us suppose that S is infinite and also $\mathbb{N} \setminus S$ is infinite. The sequence

$$\left\{ \frac{\sum_{\substack{j \leq N \\ j \in S}} c_j}{c_N} \right\}_{N=1}^{\infty}$$

will tend for $N \in S$ to 1 and for $N \in \mathbb{N} - S$ to 0. Because the sets $S, \mathbb{N} - S$ are infinte, the 0 and 1 are the cluster points, and so

$$\underline{d}_c(S) = \liminf_{N \to \infty} \frac{1}{S(N)} \sum_{\substack{j \leq N \\ j \in S}} c_j = \liminf_{N \to \infty} \frac{\sum_{\substack{j \leq N \\ j \in S}} c_j}{c_N} = 0,$$

and

$$\overline{d}_c(S) = \limsup_{N \to \infty} \frac{1}{S(N)} \sum_{\substack{j \leq N \\ j \in S}} c_j = \limsup_{N \to \infty} \frac{\sum_{\substack{j \leq N \\ j \in S}} c_j}{c_N} = 1,$$

and the set S is not measurable. In the case S is finite, then

$$\underline{d}_c(S) = \liminf_{N \to \infty} \frac{1}{S(N)} \sum_{\substack{j \leq N \\ j \in S}} c_j = 0 = \limsup_{N \to \infty} \frac{1}{S(N)} \sum_{\substack{j \leq N \\ j \in S}} c_j = \overline{d}_c(S),$$

and the $d_c(\mathbb{N} - S) = 1 - d_c(S) = 1$. Analogously for $\mathbb{N} - S$ is finite. For every g, the image of the finite set S is the finite set $g(S)$ and so $d_c(S) = d_c(g(S)) = 0$, analogously for the case $\mathbb{N} - S$ is finite. □

Lemma 2: Let the weights be not increasing and satisfy

$$\lim_{N \to \infty} \frac{N c_N}{S(N)} = 0.$$

Then if for permutation g is $\lim\limits_{j \to \infty} \frac{c_{g(j)}}{c_j} = 1$, **then** $g \in G_c$.

Proof: Let the weights not increase and satisfy the

$$\lim_{N \to \infty} \frac{N c_N}{S(N)} = 0.$$

Then if there exist the constants k_1, k_2 such that $0 < k_1 \leq \frac{c_n}{c_{g(n)}} \leq k_2 < \infty$, then we have $c_n \leq k_2 c_{g(n)}$, and so $\sum\limits_{\substack{j \leq N \\ g(j) > N}} c_j \leq k_2 \sum\limits_{\substack{j \leq N \\ g(j) > N}} c_{g(j)} \leq k_2 N c_N,$, because the weights are not increasing. So the

$$\lim_{N \to \infty} \frac{1}{S(N)} \sum_{\substack{j \leq N \\ g(j) > N}} c_j \leq \lim_{N \to \infty} \frac{1}{S(N)} k_2 N c_N = 0.$$

Analogously for the second limit, we have $0 < \frac{1}{k_2} \leq \frac{c_{g(j)}}{c_j} \leq \frac{1}{k_1} < \infty$, so $c_{g(j)} \leq \frac{1}{k_1} c_j$ and $\sum\limits_{\substack{j > N \\ g(j) \leq N}} c_{g(j)} \leq \frac{1}{k_1} \sum\limits_{\substack{j > N \\ g(j) \leq N}} c_j \leq \frac{1}{k_1} N c_N$, and

$$\lim_{N \to \infty} \frac{1}{S(N)} \sum_{\substack{j > N \\ g(j) \leq N}} c_{g(j)} \leq \lim_{N \to \infty} \frac{1}{S(N)} \frac{1}{k_1} N c_N = 0.$$

If the $\lim\limits_{j \to \infty} \frac{c_{g(j)}}{c_j} = 1$, then the existence of the constants k_1, k_2 is guaranteed, so the proof is completed. □

A special case of weighted asymptotic density is the logarithmic density, where the weights are $c_j = \frac{1}{j}$, and the $\lim\limits_{N \to \infty} \frac{N c_N}{S(N)} = \lim\limits_{N \to \infty} \frac{N \frac{1}{N}}{S(N)} = 0$, so the condition of previous lemma is satisfied. The next corollary follows immediately from the lemma.

Corollary. Let $d_c(A)$ be the logarithmic density and let g be a permutation. If $\lim\limits_{j \to \infty} \frac{c_{g(j)}}{c_j} = 1$, then g preserves the logarithmic density.

Remark. It is easy to see that the condition $\lim\limits_{j\to\infty} \frac{c_{g(j)}}{c_j} = 1$ for the weights c_j and the g can be replaced by the weaker condition stat-lim $\frac{c_{g(j)}}{c_j} = 1$, and all the statements will also hold.

Now we prove a special condition for a specific type of weights. Suppose that the sequence of weights $\{c_n\}$ has moreover two following properties:
For two sequences of positive integers $\{n\}, \{k(n)\}$ such that $k(n) \to \infty, n \to \infty$ we have

$$\lim_{n\to\infty} \frac{n}{k(n)} = 1 \Longrightarrow \lim_{n\to\infty} \frac{c_n}{c_{k(n)}} = 1. \tag{10}$$

There exists a positive real valued function $\omega(\delta)$ that $\lim_{\delta\to 1} \omega(\delta) = 1$, and

$$\lim_{N\to\infty} \frac{S(\delta N)}{S(N)} = \omega(\delta). \tag{11}$$

Theorem 6. Let the weights $\{c_n\}$ satisfy conditions (4) and (5). Then for every $g : \mathbb{N} \to \mathbb{N}$ such that

$$\lim_{n\to\infty} \frac{g(n)}{n} = 1, \tag{12}$$

and for every set $A \subset \mathbb{N}$ there holds: If A has the weighted density, then also its image $g(A)$ has the weighted density and $d_c(A) = d_c(g(A))$.

Proof: Let the set $A \subset \mathbb{N}$ have the weighted density. If A is a finite set, then $g(A)$ is also a finite one, and the assertion holds. Suppose that A is an infinite set. Let us choose an arbitrary $\varepsilon > 0$. Then the condition (12) implies that

$$(1 - \varepsilon)n \le g(n) \le (1 + \varepsilon)n, \ n \ge n_0 \tag{13}$$

for suitable $n_0 \in \mathbb{N}$. The set A can be decomposed into two subsets $A = A_0 \cup A_1$, where $A_0 = A \cap [0, n_0)$. Clearly it holds $d_c(A) = d_c(A_1), d_c(g(A_0)) = 0$. Analogously we have $\overline{d}_c(g(A_1)) = \overline{d}_c(g(A))$ and $\underline{d}_c(g(A_1)) = \underline{d}_c(g(A))$.
There holds

$$S(g(A_1), N) = \sum_{\substack{g(a)\le N \\ a\in A_1}} c_{g(a)}.$$

From the inequalities (13) we obtain

$$\sum_{\substack{a\le \frac{N}{1+\varepsilon} \\ a\in A_1}} c_{g(a)} \le S(g(A_1), N) \le \sum_{\substack{a\le \frac{N}{1-\varepsilon} \\ a\in A_1}} c_{g(a)}. \tag{14}$$

The conditions (10) and (12) imply that $\frac{c_{g(a)}}{c_a} \to 1$ as $a \to \infty$. Thus if $\sum_{a\in A} c_a < \infty$, then also $\sum_{g(a)\in g(A)} c_{g(a)} < \infty$ and $d_c(A) = d_c(g(A)) = 0$. Suppose now $\sum_{a\in A} c_a = \infty$. From Theorem of Stolz we obtain for arbitrary $\delta > 0$

$$\sum_{\substack{a\le \delta N \\ a\in A_1}} c_{g(a)} \sim S(A_1, \delta N), \ N \to \infty. \tag{15}$$

Now from (15) and (11) we have for $\delta > 0$

$$\frac{1}{S(N)} \sum_{\substack{a \leq \delta N \\ a \in A_1}} c_{g(a)} \to \omega(\delta) d(A), \ N \to \infty.$$

And so from (5) we obtain

$$\omega(\frac{1}{1+\varepsilon}) d_c(A) \leq \underline{d}_c(g(A)) \leq \overline{d}_c(g(A)) \leq \omega(\frac{1}{1-\varepsilon}) d_c(A).$$

Thus for $\varepsilon \to 0^+$ the condition () yields $d_c(A) = d_c(g(A))$. $\qquad\square$

The mappings preserving "to have density"

We conclude with the result from [BMT], announced on the page 23 which include the result of M. B. Nathanson and R. Parikh, [NP], and some cases of weight density.

Let us consider that we have a sequence $\{\nu_n\}$ of probability measures defined on $P(\mathbb{N})$. Let for every $n = 1, \dots$ there holds

i) $\nu_n(\{1, 2, \dots, n\}) = 1.$

We say that a set $A \subset \mathbb{N}$ has *generalised asymptotic density* if and only if there exists the limit $\lim_n \nu_n(A) := \nu(A)$. The value $\nu(A)$ shall be called *generalized asymptotic density* of A. Generally for arbitrary set $A \subset \mathbb{N}$ we can define *upper generalized asymptotic density* as $\limsup_n \nu_n(A) := \overline{\nu}(A)$ and *lower generalized asymptotic density* as $\liminf_n \nu_n(A) := \underline{\nu}(A)$, similarly as in the previous cases. Let us denote by $\mathcal{D}_\nu$ the system of all subsets of $\mathbb{N}$ having the generalized asymptotic density. Let us remark that this concept of density is equivalent with so called matrix density where we consider the matrix limit with respect to infinite matrix $H = \{h_{n,k}\}$, where $h_{n,k} = \nu_n(\{k\}), k, n = 1, 2, \dots$, (see [GP], [PET], [PEY]). Immediately we get:

Proposition. $\mathcal{D}_\nu$ is a q- algebra and ν is a finitely additive probability measure on $\mathcal{D}_\nu$.

We start our considerations with formally more general assertion:

Theorem A. Let $\mathcal{A}$ be an q-algebra of sets of positive integers an h a finitely additive probability measure on $\mathcal{A}$ which has the Darboux property on $\mathcal{A}$. Let $g : \mathbb{N} \to \mathbb{N}$ be such injective mapping that $g(A) \in \mathcal{A}$ for $A \in \mathcal{A}$ and for $A, B \in \mathcal{A}$ it holds

$$h(A) = h(B) \Rightarrow h(g(A)) = h(g(B)). \qquad (*)$$

Then for every $A \in \mathcal{A}$ we have $h(g(A)) = \lambda h(A)$, where $\lambda = h(g(\mathbb{N}))$.

Proof. Let $\frac{p}{q} \in < 0, 1 >, p, q \in \mathbb{N}$. Suppose that $A \in \mathcal{A}$ and $h(A) = \frac{p}{q}$. Using the Darboux propery we understand that there is a decomposition

$$\mathbb{N} = B_1 \cup \dots \cup B_q, B_j \in \mathcal{A}, h(B_j) = \frac{1}{q}, j = 1, \dots, q,$$

thus

$$g(\mathbb{N}) = g(B_1) \cup \dots \cup g(B_q), g(B_j) \in \mathcal{A}.$$

From $(*)$ we obtain $h(g(B_j)) = \frac{\lambda}{q}, j = 1, ..., q$. The set A can be decomposed into $A = A_1 \cup ... \cup A_p$, $A_i \in \mathcal{A}, h(A_i) = \frac{1}{q}, i = 1, ..., p$. Thus we have a decomposition $g(A) = g(A_1) \cup ... \cup g(A_p)$, $g(A_i) \in \mathcal{A}$. From $(*)$ we get $h(g(A_i)) = \frac{\lambda}{q}, i = 1, ..., p$, and so $h(g(A)) = \lambda\frac{p}{q}$.

Now we shall consider a function $\bar{g} :< 0, 1 > \to < 0, \lambda >$ defined as follows: if $x \in < 0, 1 >$ then exists $A \in \mathcal{A}$ that $h(A) = x$. Put $\bar{g}(x) = h(g(A))$. The condition $(*)$ provides that this definition is correct, and from the Darboux property of h on $\mathcal{A}$ we get that $\bar{g}$ is non decreasing on $< 0, 1 >$. We proved that $\bar{g}(x) = \lambda x$ for x rational and so $\bar{g}(x) = \lambda x$ for every $x \in < 0, 1 >$. $\qquad\square$

Theorem B. Suppose that following conditions are satisfied:

ii) **Every finite set F belongs to $\mathcal{D}_\nu$ and $\nu(F) = 0$.**

iii) **There exists a positive constant θ that $m, n \in \mathbb{N}, n \leq m$ and $A, B \subset \{1, ..., n\}$ there holds $|\nu_m(A) - \nu_m(B)| \leq \theta|\nu_n(A) - \nu_n(B)|$.**
Then for every injective mapping $g : \mathbb{N} \to \mathbb{N}$ such that

iv) $A \in \mathcal{D}_\nu \Rightarrow g(A) \in \mathcal{D}_\nu$
it holds
$$\nu(A) = \nu(B) \Longrightarrow \nu(g(A)) = \nu(g(B)), \ A, B \in \mathcal{D}_\nu.$$

Proof: Suppose that for some $A, B \in \mathcal{D}_\nu$ we have $\nu(A) = \nu(B)$ and $\nu(g(A)) < \nu(g(B))$. We construct a set C which contradicts iv). This set will have form

$$C = \left(\bigcup_{k=1}^\infty A \cap (m_{2k-1}, m_{2k} > \right) \cup \left(\bigcup_{k=1}^\infty B \cap (m_{2k}, m_{2k+1} > \right),$$

where the sequence $\{m_n\}$ we construct inductively. Put $\gamma = \nu(A) = \nu(B)$, $m_0 = 1$. Assume that the values $m_1, ..., m_{2k}$ are selected such that for $1 \leq l \leq k$ the following inequalities holds:

$$|\nu_{m_{2l-1}}(A) - \nu_{m_{2l-1}}(C)| \leq \frac{1}{\theta l} \tag{1}$$

$$|\nu_{m_{2l}}(B) - \nu_{m_{2l}}(C)| \leq \frac{1}{\theta(l+1)} \tag{2}$$

For $p > m_{2l-1}$

$$|\nu_p(A) - \gamma| \leq \frac{1}{l}, \tag{3}$$

and

$$|\nu_p(B) - \gamma| \leq \frac{1}{l+1} \tag{4}$$

for $p > m_{2l}$.

$$|\nu_{m_{2l}}(g(A)) - \nu_{m_{2l}}(g(C))| \leq \frac{1}{l}, \tag{5}$$

$$|\nu_{m_{2l-1}}(g(B)) - \nu_{m_{2l-1}}(g(C))| \leq \frac{1}{l}, \tag{6}$$

for $j \in (m_{2k-1}, m_{2k+1} >$ we have

$$|\nu_j(C) - \gamma| \leq \frac{2}{j}. \tag{7}$$

The condition ii) yields that for arbitrary $S_1, S_2 \in \mathcal{D}_\nu$ we have

$$S_1 \simeq S_2 \Longrightarrow \nu(S_1) = \nu(S_2). \tag{8}$$

Thus the equality $\nu(A) = \nu(B)$ and the form of C yield that exist $h_1 > m_{2k}$ that for $j \geq h_1$ we have

$$|\nu_j(A) - \nu_j(C\cap < 1, m_{2k} >) \cup (B \cap (m_{2k}, j >)| \leq \frac{1}{\theta(k+1)}.$$

Similarly we get that there exists an integer h_2 that for $j > h_2$ it holds

$$|\nu_j(A) - \gamma| \leq \frac{1}{k+1}, |\nu_j(B) - \gamma| \leq \frac{1}{k+1}.$$

The assumption iv) and (8) imply that there exists $h_3 > m_{2k}$ that

$$|\nu_j(g(B)) - \nu_j(g(C\cap < 1, m_{2k} >) \cup (B \cap (m_{2k}, j >))| \leq \frac{1}{(k+1)}$$

for $j > h_3$. Put $m_{2k+1} = \max\{h_1, h_2, h_3\}$. Then the inequalities (1), (3), (6) hold for $l = k+1$. Let i be such positive integer that $m_{2k} + i \leq m_{2k+1}$, then from (2) and (4) we get by iii)

$$|\nu_{m_{2k}+i}(C) - \gamma| = |\nu_{m_{2k}+i}((C\cap < 1, m_{2k} > \cup(B \cap (m_{2k}, m_{2k} + i >)) - \gamma| \leq$$

$$\leq |\nu_{m_{2k}+i}(B\cap < 1, m_{2k} >) + \nu_{m_{2k}+i}(B \cap (m_{2k}, m_{2k} + 1 >) - \gamma| + \frac{1}{k+1} =$$

$$= |\nu_{m_{2k}+i}(B) - \gamma| + \frac{1}{k+1} \leq \frac{2}{k+1}.$$

Analogously we can choice m_{2k+2} that (2), (4) and (5) hold for $l = k+1$ and (7) holds for $j \in (m_{2k+1}, m_{2k+2} >$. Thus $C \in \mathcal{D}_\nu$. From the other side (5) and (6) imply $\underline{\nu}(g(C)) \leq \nu(g(A)) < \nu(g(B)) \leq \overline{\nu}(g(C))$ and so $g(C)$ does not belong to $\mathcal{D}_\nu$ - contradiction. $\square$

If we consider $\nu_n(A) = \frac{A(n)}{n}, n = 1, 2, ..$ then Theorem A implies the result from [NP]. For $\nu_n(A) = \frac{S(A,n)}{S(n)}, n = 1, 2, ...$ the condition iii) is satisfied but must be provided the Darboux property. Thus we obtain

Theorem C. If $\{c_n\}$ is such sequence of weights that d_c has the Darboux property on D_c then for every injective mapping $g : \mathbb{N} \to \mathbb{N}$ such that $g(A) \in \mathcal{D}_c$ for $A \in \mathcal{D}_c$, we have $d_c(g(A)) = \lambda d_c(A)$, where $\lambda = d_c(g(\mathbb{N}))$.

The Darboux property of weight density is characterized in Theorem 3, page 84.

References

[A]   ALEXANDER, R., *Density and multiplicative structure of sets of integers*, Acta Arith. 12, 1967, 321- 332

[BAN]   BANACH S., *On the problem of the measure*, Fund. Math. 4, 1923, 4 – 33.

[B]   A.S.BESICOVITCH, *Almost periodic functions*, Dover, New York, 1954

[BF]   T.C. BROWN, A.R. FREEDMAN, *The uniform density of sets of integers and Fermat last theorem*, C. R. Math. Rep. Acad. Sci. Canada, XII, 1990, 1-6

[BLS]   BALÁŽ, V., LIARDET, P., STRAUCH, O., *Distribution functions of the sequence* $\frac{\varphi(M)}{M}$, $M \in$ $(K, K + N]$ *as K, N go to infinity*, INTEGERS 10, 2010, 705 - 732

[BMT]   J. BUKOR, L. MIŠÍK, J. TOTH, *On mappings preserving measurability*, Information sciences, 2013, 323 - 328

[BUC]   R.C.BUCK, *The measure theoretic approach to density*, Amer. J. Math **68**, 1946, 560–580

[DAB]   H. DABOUSSI, *On the density of direct factors of the set of positive integers* London Math. Soc. (2), **18**, 1978, 1 – 4

[D-M]   A. DIJKSMA, H. G. MEIJER, *Note on uniformly sequences of integers*, Nieuw Arch voor wiskunde (3), 17, 1969, 210 – 213.

[D-T]   M. DRMOTA, R.F. TICHY, *Sequences, Discrepancies and Applications, Springer, Berlin Heidelberg*, Springer, Berlin Heidelberg, 1997

[E]   P.D.T.A. ELLIOTT, *Probabilistic Number Theory I* Springer-Verlag New York, Heidelberg, Berlin, 1979

[EK]   ESTRADA, R.; KANWAL, R.P., *Series that converge on sets of null density*. Proc. Am. Math. Soc. 97, 682-686 (1986).

[Er]   ERDÖS, P., *On the density of some sequences of numbers I,*. Jornal of the London Math. Soc. 10, (1935), 120 - 125.

[Er1]   ERDÖS, P., *On the density of some sequences of numbers II*. Jornal of the London Math. Soc. 12, (1937), 7 - 11.

[ESV]   ERDÖS, P., SAFFARI, B., VAUGHAN, R. C. *On the asymptotic density of sets of integers I, II* J. Lond. Math. Soc., II. Ser. 19, 17-20 (1979), 17 – 20.

[F]   M. FEKETE, *Ueber die Verteilung der Wurzeln bei gewissen algebreischen Gleichungen mit ganzzahligen Koefizienten* Math. Zeitschr. 17, 228 - 249 1923

[Fa]   G. FALTINGS, *Endlichkeitsatze fur Abelsche Varietaten uber Zahlkorpern* Invent. Math. 73, 1983, 349 - 366

[FG]   A. FUCHS, R. GIULIANO ANTONINI, *Theorie generale des densites* , Rend. Acad. Naz. Sci., XL, Mem. Mat. (5), 1990, 253 – 294.

[FH]   H. FAST, *Sur la convergence statistique* Colloq. Math. 2, 1951, 241 - 244

[Fr]   G. A. FRIDY, *On statistical convergence*, Analysis 5, 1985, 301 – 313.

[G]   GREKOS, G, *On various definitions of density (a survey)*, Tatra Mt. Math. Publ., 31, 2005, 17–27.

[G1]   GREKOS, G., *The density set (a survey)*, Tatra Mt. Math. Publ., 31, 2005, 103–111.

[G2]   GREKOS, G., *Repartition des densites des sous suites d'une suite d'entiers*, J. Number Theory, 10, 1978, 177 - 191. 2005, 103–111.

[GA]   R. GIULIANO ANTONINI., *Sulla nozione astratta di densita in N e sul problema di prima cifra decimale* , Note Mat 4, 1984, 97 – 111.

[GLS]   Z. GALIKOVA, B. LAZSLO, T. SALAT., *Remarks on uniform density of Integers*, Acta Acad. Paed. Agriensis, Sectio Mathematicae 29, 2002, 3–13.

[GP]   R. GIULIANO ANTONINI, PASTEKA, M., *Comparison theorem for matrix limitation methods with applications*, Uniform Distribution Theory 1, 2006, 87 – 109.

[GTT]   GREKOS, G., TOMA, V,. TOMANOVA, J., *A note on uniform or Banach density*, Annales Matematiques Blaise Pascal,vol. 17, no.1, 2010,153 - 163.

[HB]   HEATH - BROWN, D., *Fermat's Last Theorem for almost all exponents*, Annales Bull. London Math. Soc., 17, 1985, 15 - 16.

[HR]   HALBERSTAM,H., ROTH. K. F., *Sequences*, Springer Verlag GmBH, 1983

[K-N]   L. KUIPERS, H. NIEDERREITER., *Uniform distribution of Sequences*, John Wiley and Sons, N.Y. London, Sydney Toronto, 1974

[KOL]   M. KOLIBIAR A KOLEKTIV, (M. KOLIBIAR, A. LEGÉŇ, T. ŠALÁT, Š. ZNÁM)., *Algebra a pribuzne discipliny, (in slovak)*, ALFA, Bratislava, 1990

[LEV]   LEVY. P., *Problemes concrets d Analyse Fonctionelle*, Gauthier Villars **Paris**, 1951.

[M]   D.MAHARAM, *Finitelly additive measures on integers*, Sankhya 38, 1976, 44 - 59

[Mi]   L. MIŠÍK, *Sets of positive integers with prescribed values of densities*, Math. Slovaca 52, 2002, 289 - 296

[MMST]   MAČAJ, M., MIŠÍK, L ŠALÁT, T., TOMANOVÁ J, *On a class of of densities of positive integers*, Acta Math. Univ. Comenianae **LXXII**, 2 2003, 213-221.

[N]   NOVOSELOV, E. V., *Topological theory of polyadic numbers*, Trudy Tbilis. Mat. Inst. 27, 61 - 69, (1960), in russian

[N1]   NOVOSELOV, E. V., *New method in the probability number theory*, Doklady akademii nauk. ser. matem. No. 2, 28, 307 - 364, (1964), in russian

[NAR]   NARKIEWICZ, W, *Teoria liczb*, (in polish) PWN, Warszawa, 1991

[NIV]   NIVEN, I., *The asymptotic density of sequences*, Bull. Amer. Math. Soc. 57, 1951, 420–434

[NIV1]   NIVEN, I., *Uniform distribution of sequences of integers*, Trans. Amer. Math. Soc. 98, 52 - 61

[NP]   NATHANSON, M. B.–PARIKH, R., *Density of sets of natural numbers nad the Lévy group*, J. Number Theory,**124**, 2007, 151-157

[OB]   OBATA, N., *Density of natural numbers and Lévy group*, J. Number Theory **30**, 1988, 288-297.

[P]   R.G. POSTNIKOV, *Introduction to analytic number theory, (in russian)*, Moscov, Nauka, 1971, english translation: Amer Math Soc, Providence RI 1981

[Pa]   M. PARNES, *On the measure of measurable sets of integers*, Acta Arith. XXV, 1973, 51–54

[PAS]   M. PAŠTÉKA, *Some properties of Buck's measure density*, Math. Slovaca 42, no. 1, 1992, 15-32

[PAS2]   M. PAŠTÉKA, *measure density of some sets*, Math. Slovaca 44, no. 5, 1994, 515 - 524

[PAS3]   M. PAŠTÉKA, *Remarks on one type of uniform distribution* Unif. Distrib. Theory 2, No. 1, 79-92 (2007).

[PAS4]   M. PAŠTÉKA, *A note about the submeasures and Fermat last theorem* Ricerche Mat.,XLIII,1994,79–90

[PAS5]   M. PAŠTÉKA, *Note on the permutations which preserve Buck's measure density*. Mediterr. J. Math.6, No. 1, 125-134 (2009).

[PAS6]   M. PAŠTÉKA, *Note on a subgroup of L vy's group*. Math. Slovac 58, No. 5, 535-540 (2008).

[PAS7]   M. PAŠTÉKA, *The measurability of the product of arithmetic progressions*. Tatra Mt. Math. Publ. 34, No. 1, 107-111 (2006).

[PAS9]   M. PAŠTÉKA, *Remarks on Buck's measure density*. Tatra Mt. Math. Publ. 3, 191-200 (1993).

[PAS10] M. PAŠTÉKA, *Convergence of series and submeasures of the set of positive integers*. Math. Slovaca 40, No.3, 273-278 (1990).

[PET]   PETERSEN, G.M., *Regular Matrix Transformations*, McGraw-Hill Publishing Co., Ltd., London-New York-Toronto, Ont. 1966.

[PEY]   PEYERIMHOFF, A., *Lectures on Summability*, Lecture Notes in Mathematics Vol. 107, Springer-Verlag, Berlin-New York, 1969.

[PL]   Š. PORUBSKÝ, F. LUCA, *On asymptotic and logarithmic densities*, Tatra Mt. Math. Publ. **31**, 2005, 75–86.

[PSS]   Š. PORUBSKÝ, O. STRAUCH, T. ŠALÁT, *Transformations that preserve uniform distribution*, Acta Arith. 43, 1988, 459–479

[PSV]   PAŠTÉKA, M., ŠALÁT, T., VISNYAI, T., *Remarks on Buck's measure density and a generalization of asymptotic density*, Tatra Mt. Math. Publ. **31**, 2005, 87-101.

[P-T]   PASTEKA, M., TICHY, R., *A note on the corration coefficient of arithmetic functions*, Acta Acad. Paed. Agriensis, Sectio Mathematicae 30, 2003, 109–114.

[PV]   M. PAŠTÉKA, Z. VÁCLAVÍKOVÁ, *Some remarks on permutations which preserve the weighted density*. Tatra Mt. Math. Publ. to appear.

[R]   P. RIBENBOIM, *Density results on families on diophantine equations with finitelly many solutions*, L' Enseignement matematique 39, 1980, 3 - 23.

[Re]   RÉNYI, A., *Warscheindlichkheitstheorie*, Gauthier Teubner Verlag VEB BERLIN.

[Re1]   RÉNYI, A., *On the density of certain sequences of integers*, Publ. Inst. Math. Acad. Serb. Sci., 1951, 157 - 162.

[S]   O. STRAUCH., *Two properties of the sequence u.d.(mod 1)*, Acta Math. Univ. Comenianae, 1984, 67–73

[SAF]   SAFFARI, B., *On the asymptotic density of sets of integers*. J. Lond. Math. Soc., II. Ser. 13, 475-485 (1976).

[Sal]   T. ŠALÁT, *On statistically convergent sequences of real numbers*, Math. Slovaca 30, No 2, 1980, 139 - 150.

[Sal2]   T. ŠALÁT, *On the function* $\alpha_p, p^{\alpha_p(n)}||n, (n > 1)$, Math. Slovaca 44, 1994, 143 - 151.

[SaS]   T. ŠALÁT, A. SCHINZEL, *Remarks on maximum and minimum exponents in factoring*, Math. Slovaca 44, no. 5, 1994, 505 – 514

[S-B]   SHAFAREVICH, BOREVICH, Z, *Theory of Numbers*, (in polish) Nauka, Moscow, 1972

[Sch]   I. SCHOENBERG, *Über die asymptotische Verteilung reeler Zahlen mod 1.*, Math. Z., 1928, 171–199.

[SP]   O. STRAUCH, Š. PORUBSKÝ, *Distribution of Sequences a Sampler*, Peter Lang, SAV, Frankfurt am Main, Peter Lang, SAV, Frankfurt am Main, 2005

[S-T]   T. ŠALÁT, TIJDEMAN, R., *Asymptotic densities of sets of positive integers*, Math. Slovaca 33, 1983, 199–207

[S-To]   T. ŠALÁT, TOMANOVA, J., *On the product of divisors of a positive integer*, Math. Slovaca 52, 2002, 271–278

[ST]   STEIN, S. K., *The density of product of arithmetic progression*, Fibonacci Quart., 11, 1973, 145–152

[SZ]   SLEZIAK, M., ZIMAN, M., *Levy group and density measures* , J. Number Theory, 128, 2008, 3005–3012

[WEY]   H. WEYL, *Uber die Gleichverteilung von Zahlen mod. Eins*, Math. Ann, 1916, 77, 313–352

Index

additive, 7, 22, 23, 32, 33, 35, 38, 91, 95
algebra, 42
algebra , 38, 39, 54, 91
arithmetic function, 17, 18, 29–34, 44, 49,
    50, 57, 71, 72
arithmetic progression, 32, 38, 40, 49, 53,
    54, 61–63, 65, 67, 96
asymptotic density, 7–10, 12, 15, 17, 21–26,
    29, 35–40, 44, 48, 57, 58, 62, 66,
    67, 70, 73, 81, 85, 87–89, 95, 96

Banach limit, 35

Chebyshev inequality, 29
complete reminder system, 65, 66
complete sequence, 46, 47, 50, 54, 63, 65
continuous, 31
continuous , 31, 32, 50, 55–58, 60, 73

Darboux, 9
direct factors, 17
Dirichlet convolution,, 17
dispersion, 30

ergodic, 64
extension, 35–37

generalized asymptotic density , 91

ideal, 8, 26–29, 45, 73, 81
increasing sequence, 9, 10, 28, 73

mean value, 29–31, 49
measurable, 39–44, 46, 47, 51, 54, 57, 58,
    67, 68, 89, 95
measure density, 8, 38–40, 42, 45, 49, 52,
    61–68, 95, 96

permutation, 8, 21–25, 61–67, 85, 89
permutation , 85, 88–90
polyadically, 56–58, 60
polyadicly, 31, 50
prime, 11, 13, 14, 16–21, 32, 33, 39–41, 44,
    58, 62, 64, 70, 72

progression, 38, 48, 50, 61, 63, 64, 83, 95

q-algebra, 11, 91

random variable, 8, 30
Riemannian integrable, 55, 60

uniform density, 8, 59, 69–73, 77, 78, 94,
    95
uniformly distributed, 31, 32, 48–56, 61

weight density, 8, 26, 82
weight density,, 81, 83
Weyl's criterion, 32, 50, 56, 73